Praise for *Six Impossible Things*

'[A]n accessible primer on all things quantum ... rigorous and chatty.'
Sunday Times

'Gribbin has inspired generations with his popular science writing, and this, his latest offering, is a compact and delightful summary of the main contenders for a true interpretation of quantum mechanics. ... If you've never puzzled over what our most successful scientific theory means, or even if you have and want to know what the latest thinking is, this new book will bring you up to speed faster than a collapsing wave function.'
Jim Al-Khalili

'Gribbin gives us a feast of precision and clarity, with a phenomenal amount of information for such a compact space. It's a TARDIS of popular science books, and I loved it. ... This could well be the best piece of writing this grand master of British popular science has ever produced, condensing as it does many years of pondering the nature of quantum physics into a compact form.'
Brian Clegg, popularscience.co.uk

'Elegant and accessible ... Highly recommended for students of the sciences and fans of science fiction, as well as for anyone who is curious to understand the strange world of quantum physics.'
Forbes

SEVEN

PILLARS OF

SCIENCE

Also by John Gribbin

Six Impossible Things: The 'Quanta of Solace'
and the Mysteries of the Subatomic World

In Search of Schrödinger's Cat

The Universe: A Biography

Schrödinger's Kittens and the Search for Reality

Computing With Quantum Cats

Einstein's Masterwork: 1915 and the General Theory of Relativity

13.8: The Quest to Find the True Age of the Universe
and the Theory of Everything

With Mary Gribbin

Richard Feynman: A Life in Science

Science: A History in 100 Experiments

Out of the Shadow of a Giant: How Newton Stood
on the Shoulders of Hooke and Halley

SEVEN

PILLARS OF

SCIENCE

*The Incredible Lightness
of Ice, and Other
Scientific Surprises*

JOHN

GRIBBIN

ICON

Published in the UK in 2020
by Icon Books Ltd, Omnibus Business Centre,
39–41 North Road, London N7 9DP
email: info@iconbooks.com
www.iconbooks.com

Sold in the UK, Europe and Asia
by Faber & Faber Ltd, Bloomsbury House,
74–77 Great Russell Street,
London WC1B 3DA or their agents

Distributed in the UK, Europe and Asia
by Grantham Book Services, Trent Road,
Grantham NG31 7XQ

Distributed in Australia and New Zealand
by Allen & Unwin Pty Ltd, PO Box 8500,
83 Alexander Street, Crows Nest, NSW 2065

Distributed in South Africa
by Jonathan Ball, Office B4, The District,
41 Sir Lowry Road, Woodstock 7925

ISBN: 978-178578-656-3

Typeset in Whitman by Marie Doherty

Printed and bound in Great Britain by
Clays Ltd, Elcograf S.p.A.

CONTENTS

John Gribbin's numerous bestselling books include *In Search of Schrödinger's Cat*, *The Universe: A Biography*, *13.8: The Quest to Find the True Age of the Universe and the Theory of Everything*, and *Out of the Shadow of a Giant: How Newton Stood on the Shoulders of Hooke and Halley*.

His most recent book is *Six Impossible Things: The 'Quanta of Solace' and the Mysteries of the Subatomic World*, which was shortlisted for the Royal Society Insight Investment Science Book Prize for 2019.

He is a Visiting Fellow at the University of Sussex, and was described as 'one of the finest and most prolific writers of popular science around' by the *Spectator*.

ACKNOWLEDGEMENTS

I am grateful to the Alfred C. Munger Foundation for financial support while writing this book, and to the University of Sussex for providing a base and research facilities.

As with all my books, Mary Gribbin ensured that I did not stray too far into the thickets of incomprehensibility. The remaining infelicities are all mine.

LIST OF ILLUSTRATIONS

Wisdom hath builded her house, she hath hewn out her seven pillars.

Proverbs 9:1

PREFACE

Seven Pillars of Wisdom

J.B.S. Haldane famously described the four stages of acceptance for scientific ideas as:

i)   this is worthless nonsense;
ii) this is an interesting, but perverse, point of view;
iii) this is true, but quite unimportant;
iv) I always said so.

The more I look at the history of science – and the longer I observe the ongoing development of science – the more I appreciate the truth of this aphorism. Looking back, it is easy to see how ideas that were once outrageous became accepted truths, and to feel a sense of superiority over those simpletons who, for example, thought that the Earth was flat. But even in my own lifetime I have seen ideas once regarded as wild speculations – including the Big Bang theory of the origin of the Universe and the non-locality of quantum entities – become received wisdom, pillars of science, while more 'commonsensical' alternatives – the Steady State theory, the idea that what happens in one location cannot instantly affect what happens somewhere far away – have fallen by the wayside. How science works is as fascinating as the science itself, and to demonstrate this I have picked out seven examples which were each sensational in their day, and which have either become pillars of scientific wisdom or are well on their way to passing through Haldane's four stages of acceptance. In order to restrict myself to seven, I needed some overall theme to link them, and I have chosen features of the Universe which are closely related to our own existence, and to the possibility of life elsewhere. This is, after all, the most important aspect of science as far as we humans are concerned.

Some of these examples are already pillars of science, others may be at an earlier stage – I leave you to judge which ones. But although all were sensational in their day, and some still are, a key feature of the development of science is a willingness to think the unthinkable, and then, crucially, to test those ideas and find out if they are good descriptions of what is going on in the real world. There are, though, some ideas which are impossible to categorise, and which, depending on your personal point of view, might be assigned to any one of Haldane's stages. The biggest of these is a question that has puzzled philosophers for much longer than what we call science has existed, and with which I shall top and tail this book – are we alone in the Universe?

John Gribbin
November 2019

Worlds Beyond:
Maybe We Are Not Alone

The Earth is round and moves through space. This was a dramatic realisation only a few hundred years ago. It flies in the face of common sense, so much so that some people still cannot accept it. You may not be one of those people, but do you just accept the story because it is what you were told as a child and 'everybody knows' it is true? Or have you ever stopped to think what a crazy idea this is, in terms of your everyday experience, and to consider the evidence?

To see how reasonable the idea of a flat Earth is, and how sensational was the realisation that it is round, we can look back to the Greek philosopher Anaxagoras of Athens, who was around in the fifth century BCE. Anaxagoras was no fool. He based his reasoning on the best evidence available to him, and given those facts his reasoning was correct. His conclusions turn out to have been wrong, but far more important than that is the fact that he tried to understand the Sun as a physical entity subject to the same laws as those that apply to things here on Earth. He did not treat it as a supernatural phenomenon beyond human comprehension.

The trigger for Anaxagoras' speculations was a meteorite which fell one day at Aegospotami. The meteorite was hot, so he inferred that it must have come from the Sun. It contained iron, so he inferred that the Sun must be made of iron – a hot ball of iron travelling across the sky. All this was completely logical in the light of the state of knowledge at the time. But it raised two intriguing questions that Anaxagoras set out to answer – how big must that ball of hot iron be, and how far above the surface of the Earth was it moving?

Anaxagoras wasn't much of a traveller, but he had heard accounts from people who had been to the Nile delta, and beyond to the upper reaches of the Nile. These accounts mentioned that at the stroke of noon on the summer solstice (the 'longest day'), the Sun was vertically overhead at a city called Syene, near the present-day location of the Aswan dam. You may have come across this tit-bit of information in another context; if so, be prepared for a surprise. Anaxagoras also knew that on the longest day at noon the Sun was at an angle of 7 degrees out of the vertical at the Nile delta. And he knew the distance from the delta to Syene. With this information, assuming the Earth was flat and using the geometry of right-angled triangles, it was a trivial matter for Anaxagoras to calculate that at noon on the summer solstice the Sun was roughly 4,000 miles (in modern units) above the heads of the inhabitants of Syene. Because the Sun covers roughly half a degree of arc on the sky (the same as the Moon, a dramatic coincidence outside the scope of this book), the geometry of triangles also told him that it must be about 35 miles across, roughly the same as the southern peninsula of Greece, the Peloponnesus.

The suggestion that the Sun was a natural phenomenon was so shocking to his fellow citizens that Anaxagoras was arrested for heresy, and banished for ever from his home city of Athens. It would be more than two thousand years, not until the seventeenth century, before another thinker, Galileo Galilei, also tried to explain the Sun as a natural phenomenon, and was also accused of heresy.

But only a couple of hundred years after Anaxagoras another Greek philosopher, Eratosthenes, used exactly the same data in a slightly different calculation. This is the version of the story you may have heard. Eratosthenes assumed that the Earth is spherical, and guessed that the Sun is so far away that rays of light from the Sun reach the Earth along parallel lines. With this assumption, the angle of 7 degrees out of the vertical measured at the Nile delta is the same as the angle subtended at the surface of the Earth by the distance from the delta to Syene, measured from the centre of the Earth (see diagram overleaf). This makes it possible to calculate the radius of the Earth. Because the angle is the same, the 'answer' is the same – 4,000 miles. But this is now interpreted as the radius of the Earth, not the distance of the Sun above the Earth. Because Eratosthenes was 'right', his is the version of the story recorded in textbooks and popular accounts, while Anaxagoras is ignored. But the moral is not who was right and who was wrong. Good theories are based

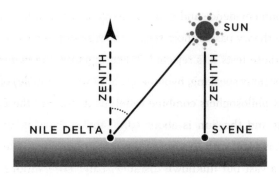

Assuming the Earth is flat,
it is simple to calculate the distance to the Sun

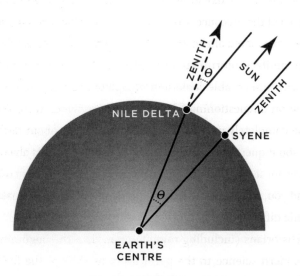

Assuming the Earth is round,
the same observation tells us the radius of the planet

4

on sound evidence and make predictions that can be tested. If the theory passes those tests, it continues to be used; if it fails those tests it is rejected. Taken together, the two theories (strictly speaking, hypotheses, but I won't quibble) of the Greek philosophers combine to tell us that either the Earth is flat and the Sun is about 4,000 miles above it, or the Earth is a ball with a radius of about 4,000 miles and the Sun is at a vast but unknown distance. Later observations and measurements made it possible to decide which is a better description of the real world.

There is also a cautionary aspect to the tale. Even a radical and far-sighted thinker who was not afraid to confront the authorities of his day in his quest for the truth could not rid himself of the preconception that the Earth is flat. Anaxagoras never considered alternatives. The history of science is filled with similar unfortunate examples of ideas that are built up with impeccable logic and complete accuracy, but are based on unquestioning faith in something which turns out to be completely untrue. Science should not be about faith, but about questioning cherished beliefs. Not that this always makes for a quiet life, as Giordano Bruno found to his cost. Mind you, Bruno seems to have gone out of his way to make his life difficult, and not just in the pursuit of science.

Historians (including myself) often date the beginning of modern science to the publication in 1543 of the book *De Revolutionibus Orbium Coelestium* (*On the Revolution of the Celestial Spheres*), by Nicolaus Copernicus. In truth, though,

Giordano Bruno
Science Photo Library

the book was not a sensation at the time; the ideas it contained did not gain widespread currency for the best part of a hundred years, and it did not go far enough in displacing ourselves from the centre of the Universe. Copernicus retained the idea that there is a fixed centre to the Universe, but moved this from the Earth to the Sun. He explained the apparent movement of the stars across the sky as due to the rotation of the Earth, but retained the idea that the stars and planets were fixed to solid spheres moving around the Sun. His most 'heretical' suggestion was that the Earth also is a planet, orbiting the Sun once a year, but that is as far as he went.

Bruno picked up Copernicus' ball and ran off with it. Born near Naples in 1548, five years after the publication of *De Revolutionibus*, and christened Filippo, Bruno joined the Dominican order at the age of seventeen, taking the name Giordano, and became an ordained priest in 1572. He soon ran into difficulties because of his free thinking and taste for forbidden (or at least, controversial) books. He seems to have got into particular trouble for espousing Arianism, the belief that Jesus occupies a position intermediate between Man and God, making him divine but not the same as God. When things became too hot, he fled Naples, discarded his religious garments, and began a series of wanderings that took him to, among other places, Geneva, Lyon and Toulouse, where he took a doctorate in theology and lectured on philosophy. In 1581 he moved to Paris, where he enjoyed the safety of the protection of the king, Henry III, and published several works.

In 1583 Bruno went to England with letters of recommendation from the French king, and moved in Elizabethan court circles where he met such notable people as Philip Sidney and (possibly) John Dee. Although he gave some lectures in Oxford on the Copernican model of the Universe, he was unable to obtain a position at the university, where his controversial views were derided by John Underhill, then Rector of Lincoln College and later Archbishop of Canterbury, who sneered at Bruno for espousing 'the opinion of Copernicus that the earth did go round, and the heavens did stand still; whereas in truth it was his own head which rather did run round, and his brains did not stand still'.[1] It appears, though, that it was as much Bruno's personality as his teaching that made him unwelcome in Oxford. He seems to have been arrogant and unwilling to give much time to people he regarded as fools, and managed to put up the backs even of people who shared his views.

But this was less than half of what Bruno proposed. In 1584 he published two of a series of 'dialogues' in which he supported the Copernican cosmology, and by 1588 he was writing that the Universe is 'infinite ... endless and limitless'. So what were the stars? Pulling together the ideas expressed by Bruno in several places, he was the first person to realise that not only are the stars other suns, but that like the Sun itself they could each have their own family of planets. These other worlds, he said, 'have no less virtue nor a nature different from that of our Earth', and therefore they could 'contain animals and inhabitants'.

This would have been enough to bring him into further conflict with the Roman Catholic authorities, and Bruno is sometimes held up as a martyr for science. But his problems with the authorities ran so deep that these beliefs actually amount to no more than a footnote in the story of his later life and fate. In 1585, because of a deteriorating political situation between England and France, Bruno returned to Paris, then on to Germany and Prague, where he achieved the distinction (having already fallen foul of the Catholic authorities) of being excommunicated by the Lutherans. In 1591 he took a chance on returning to Italy, initially to Padua in the hope of getting a professorship. But the job went to Galileo and he moved on to Venice, the most liberal of the Italian city states. Not liberal enough, as it turned out. On 22 May 1592 Bruno was arrested and charged with blasphemy and heresy, his belief in the plurality of worlds just one of many examples in the citation. He might have got away with a relatively light sentence, but the Inquisition demanded that he should be transferred to Rome for them to deal with, and the Venetian authorities eventually bowed to pressure and handed him over in February 1593.

Bruno's trial lasted for seven years, off and on, during which time he was imprisoned in Rome. Many of the papers relating to the trial have been lost, but the charges against him included not only broad-brush blasphemy and heresy but immoral conduct. Specific charges are thought to have included speaking and writing against the idea of the Trinity and the divinity of Christ, and doubting the virginity of Mary, mother of Jesus. He also made the shocking suggestion that different branches of the Christian Church should live in harmony and respect each other's views. These were much greater sins in the eyes of the Inquisition than speculating about the plurality of worlds, but that went on the list anyway.* As usual with heretics, Bruno was eventually given an opportunity to recant, which he refused, and on 20 January 1600 Pope Clement VIII formally declared him a heretic. He is alleged to have made a threatening gesture at the judges when sentenced; he was burned at the stake on 17 February 1600, having first been gagged to prevent any heretical last words being heard by the onlookers. So here are some of his not-quite-last words which demonstrate the breadth of his thinking:

> There is no absolute up or down, as Aristotle taught; no absolute position in space; but the position of a body is relative to that of other bodies. Everywhere there is incessant relative change in position throughout the universe, and the observer is always at the centre of things.

Although it quite quickly became appreciated that the stars are indeed other suns – Isaac Newton was one of several people

---

* Arguably, if it hadn't been for Bruno the Church might not have got so worked up about Copernicus – his book was only placed on the Index of banned works in 1616, and remained there until 1835.

who tried to estimate the distances to stars by assuming that they had roughly the same brightness as our Sun – it was only in the 1840s that astronomers were able to measure a few of those distances directly using the geometrical technique of parallax, which uses the shift in position of nearby stars against the background of distant stars as the Earth moves around its orbit. It was only in the twentieth century that other techniques made it possible to measure distances far out across the Universe, and eventually, by the 1930s, to make the notion of an infinite Universe respectable. But even then the idea that the stars might have their own families of planets remained pure speculation.

The situation changed in 1995, with the discovery of a planet orbiting a star, labelled 51 Pegasi, roughly similar to the Sun. The discovery was made by analysing the wobble of the star caused by the gravitational pull of the planet orbiting around it. These measurements are possible because the wobble causes a tiny shift in the spectral lines of the star,* a process known as the Doppler effect. The measurements turned out to be relatively easy, because the planet is very big and orbits rather close to the star, so it has a relatively large gravitational influence. This was not what astronomers were expecting.

In our Solar System, there are four small rocky planets (very roughly like the Earth) orbiting in the inner region nearer the Sun, and four large gaseous planets (very roughly like Jupiter)

....
* Stellar spectroscopy is one of the pillars discussed later.

orbiting in the outer regions, plus various small bits of debris including the object Pluto. With no other information to go on, astronomers guessed that other planetary systems might be similar. But the planet found orbiting 51 Pegasi is very large and orbiting very close to its star. It became known as a 'hot jupiter'. It has more than half the mass of Jupiter, the largest planet in our Solar System, and orbits its star at only a tenth of the distance of Mercury, the innermost planet in the Solar System, from our Sun. The first lesson drawn from this is that you cannot generalise on the basis of one example! Our Solar System is clearly not the only kind of planetary system in the Universe, and may even be unusual. And the corollary is that we should not assume that the Earth is a typical planet; more on this later.

Since 1995 many more 'extrasolar' planetary systems have been discovered, many of them harbouring hot jupiters, and many now known to have multiple planets, in a variety of configurations, orbiting the central stars. The discovery of a 'new' planet is no longer news, let alone headline news, unless it is what news outlets like to call an 'Earth-like' planet. But be wary of the headlines. All that they mean by this is that the planet is probably rocky and has a few times the mass of the Earth. It is Earth-sized, rather than Earth-like. And to clarify the distinction we have only to look at our nearest neighbour in the Solar System, the planet Venus, orbiting a little closer to the Sun than us. Venus is almost exactly the same size as the Earth, it is rocky, and overall it is a better candidate for the description 'Earth-like' than any of the extra-solar planets trumpeted in the media. It has a similar size, mass, density and surface gravity. But the temperature on the surface of Venus is 462°C, hot enough to melt lead. This temperature is not because the planet is slightly closer to the Sun than we are, but thanks to a strong greenhouse effect produced by its thick carbon dioxide atmosphere. The atmospheric pressure on the surface of Venus is 92 times the pressure at the surface of Earth, the same as the pressure a kilometre below the surface of our oceans.

Which brings us back to Bruno and his suggestion that there is a multitude of planets populated by a multitude of life forms, including people. Planets there are, in profusion. Every Sun-like star, and perhaps every star, seems to have a family of planets. Let's not be too pessimistic. There are hundreds of billions of stars in the Milky Way, our home galaxy, a kind of island in the Universe. Even if only a small proportion of them have planetary systems like our Solar System, and even if only a small proportion of those systems have at least one planet which is more Earth-like than Venus-like, there could be millions of potential homes for life forms like us out there, before we even consider more exotic possibilities. One per cent of 100 billion is still a billion, and one per cent of a billion is 10 million. Planets are common in the Universe – maybe even planets like Earth. Maybe we are not alone. Homes for life may be common. But what about life itself? How did we get here? The answer depends on seven surprising discoveries about the way the Universe works – seven pillars of science that underpin our existence, and the possible existence of other life in the Universe.

PILLAR

Solid Things Are Mostly Empty Space

Solid objects are empty. Although this is an often cited example of the non-commonsensical nature of the world, it still brings you up short if you stop to think about it. Things like the 'solid' keyboard I am typing on and the fingers doing the typing are made up of tiny particles spread through relatively huge volumes of space, held together by electric forces. This is such an important and mind-blowing idea that Richard Feynman said it was the most significant fact that science had discovered about the world. As on so many topics, it is worth quoting him verbatim:

> If, in some cataclysm, all of scientific knowledge were to be destroyed, and only one sentence passed on to the next generation of creatures, what statement would contain the most information in the fewest words? I believe it is the *atomic hypothesis* (or the atomic *fact*, or whatever you wish to call it) that *all things are made of atoms – little particles that move around in perpetual motion, attracting each other*

when they are a little distance apart, but repelling upon being squeezed into one another. In that one sentence, you will see, there is an enormous amount of information about the world, if just a little imagination and thinking are applied.[2]

Few physicists, however, have the power of imagination (or better, physical insight) and thinking that Feynman had, and the debate about whether the world is really made of such particles was not resolved until the early years of the twentieth century, although the idea of atoms had been suggested much earlier.

Popular accounts of the atomic theory (or whatever you wish to call it) usually start out with a nod to Democritus, who lived in the fifth century BCE, and Epicurus, who was around between about 342 BCE and 271 BCE. But their idea of little objects moving about in 'the void' and interacting with one another was never more than a minority opinion, ridiculed by philosophers such as Aristotle who rejected the idea of a void. It wasn't until 1649 that Pierre Gassendi revived the idea and suggested that atoms had different shapes and could join together through a kind of hook-and-eye mechanism. He stressed that there was nothing at all in the gaps between atoms. This was the beginning of a debate that rumbled on for more than two hundred years. On one side there was what we might call the Newtonian school of thought, after Isaac Newton, which favoured the atomic hypothesis; on the other, the Cartesian school, after René Descartes, who abhorred the idea of a void, or vacuum. Things came to a head in the nineteenth century.

From the 1850s onward, building on the earlier work of John Dalton, chemists increasingly accepted the idea of atoms, with atoms of different elements having different weights, and joining together to make molecules, so that a molecule of water, for example, was regarded as a combination of two hydrogen atoms with one oxygen atom. They could measure the weights (strictly speaking, masses) of atoms of different elements compared with that of hydrogen, the lightest element. And they were even able to calculate how many particles (atoms or molecules) there must be in a sample of any element that contained its atomic (or molecular) weight in grams – 1 gram of hydrogen, 12 grams of carbon, 16 grams of oxygen, and so on. Each such sample would have the same number of particles. This number became known as Avogadro's number, after the pioneer who developed the theory behind it, and it is very big. But before I go into how big it is, I should spell out the opposition to these ideas that persisted even at the beginning of the twentieth century, and which highlights how sensational the idea of atoms really is.

The opposition came from physicists and philosophers who pointed out what they saw as a fatal flaw in the idea of large numbers of tiny particles moving around in empty space, bouncing off each other and going merrily on their way in accordance with the laws of motion spelled out by Isaac Newton. The relevant thing about Newton's laws is that they are reversible. The standard way of highlighting this is to think of a collision between two pool balls. One ball moves in from, say, the left, hits a stationary ball and stops, while the other ball moves off to the right. If you made a movie of this event and ran it backwards, it would still look entirely OK. A ball would move in from the right, collide with a stationary ball and stop while the other ball moved off to the left. Newton's laws do not contain an 'arrow of time'. But the real world does have a direction of time built in to it. If we now imagine the cue ball striking the pack of pool balls in a break so that they scatter in all directions, the situation is not reversible, even though every single collision between the balls obeys Newton's laws. 'Running the movie backwards' produces a sequence never seen in the everyday world – balls arriving from all directions, colliding and settling into a neat pack while just one ball zooms off towards the cue.

The irreversibility of the everyday world was expressed by nineteenth-century scientists in terms of heat – the science of thermodynamics. They pointed out that heat always flows from a hotter object to a colder one. An ice cube placed in a glass of warm water gains heat from the water and melts; we never see water in a glass spontaneously getting warmer while a lump of ice forms in the middle. But both this scenario and the 'reversed' pool ball break are entirely allowed by Newton's laws. The initial conclusion of the nineteenth-century thermodynamicists was that things could not really be made of tiny particles bouncing around in accordance with those laws. But then the dilemma was resolved.

No fewer than three great thinkers independently found the solution. They realised that the behaviour of large numbers of particles interacting in accordance with Newton's laws had to be described in statistical terms, and they worked out the equations to calculate how very large numbers of particles would behave – the laws of what became known as statistical mechanics. This tells us, in a rigorous mathematical way, that although there is nothing in the laws of physics to prevent ice cubes forming in glasses of warm water, such an event is extremely unlikely, and will only occur once in a very, very long time – a time which can be calculated if you know how many particles are involved.* The first two scientists to appreciate this and work out the laws of statistical mechanics can be excused for not knowing about each other's work. Ludwig Boltzmann worked in Europe, while Willard Gibbs worked in the USA, and even at the turn of the nineteenth century scientific ideas took a while to cross the Atlantic. The third inventor (or discoverer) of statistical mechanics had less excuse, not least since he came on the scene a little later. But he was notorious for not bothering to keep up with what other people were doing, preferring to work everything out for himself. His name was Albert Einstein, and it is a sign of how the atomic theory of matter had failed to become established

....

* You would have to sit watching that glass of water for vastly longer than the present age of the Universe to have much chance of seeing an ice cube form.

that at the beginning of the twentieth century he set out to find evidence 'which would guarantee as much as possible the existence of atoms of definite finite size'.[3] His version of statistical mechanics appeared in a series of three extraordinary papers, published between 1902 and 1904, which would have assured him of scientific fame, if only he had been first on the scene. But in 1905, among other things he did produce the scientific paper which finally established the reality of atoms and molecules to all but a few die-hard philosophers. It's also much easier for non-mathematicians to grasp, so I shall cast statistical mechanics to one side and focus on the physics.

The physics harks back to an old piece of work which Einstein was at least aware of, but only in a vague sort of way. And it wasn't the jumping-off point for his own work, because once again he was working it out from first principles, this time trying to calculate how a small piece of material – such as a dust grain – suspended in a liquid – such as a glass of water – would move as it was buffeted about by atoms and molecules striking it from all sides. This kind of motion had been studied by the Scottish botanist Robert Brown back in the 1820s. His interest stemmed from observations, made using microscopes, of pollen grains dancing about in water in a jittery kind of motion, like running on the spot. The natural explanation at the time was that the pollen grains were alive, and moving under their own steam. But Brown tested this by looking at grains of ground-up glass and granite in water, and found that they danced in the same way. This established that the dancing had nothing to do with life, and it became known as Brownian motion.

Einstein started out by calculating how atoms and molecules would make inanimate dust grains move in a liquid, but starting from the bottom up, not from the top down. In the first paragraph of the paper on the subject he produced in 1905, he says:

> It is possible that the motions to be discussed here are identical with so-called Brownian molecular motion; however, the data available to me on the latter are so imprecise that I could not form a judgement on the question.

The 'data available' were 'so imprecise' because he couldn't be bothered to look them up; and there must be a strong suspicion that this sentence was added after some friend read a draft of the paper and pointed out to him the link to Brownian motion. But whatever his motivation, Einstein explained Brownian motion with one of those pieces of insight that geniuses come up with, but which then make you wonder why nobody else thought of it, backed up by calculations which gave the experimenters something to test.

Particles large enough to be seen using contemporary microscopes – grains like pollen, or ground-up glass – were, Einstein realised, far too small to be moved visibly by the impact of a single atom or molecule. But in a liquid, such particles are constantly being bombarded on all sides by large numbers of atoms and molecules. This bombardment cannot be perfectly even. At any instant, a few more impacts will occur on one side, and a few less on another. The particle will shift a little in the direction of fewer impacts. But then the balance will change, and it will be nudged in a different direction. The overall effect is that it jitters about, not quite running on the spot but jogging in a zigzag path and gradually getting further away from where it started. The path is now known as a random walk; and this was Einstein's key insight.

Einstein showed that wherever the particle starts from, the distance it moves away from that point depends on the square root of the time that has passed. So if it moves a certain distance in one second it will move twice as far in four seconds (because 2 is the square root of 4), four times as far in sixteen seconds, and so on. But it doesn't keep going in the same direction. After four seconds it is twice as far away, but in a random and unpredictable direction; after sixteen seconds it is four times as far away in another random direction. This is called 'root mean square' displacement, and it was possible for experimenters to test the prediction. Plugging in Avogadro's number from other studies, Einstein concluded that a particle with a diameter of 0.001mm in water at 17°C would shift position by six millionths of a metre from its starting point in one minute. The modern calculation of Avogadro's number, the number of molecules in the molecular weight of a substance in grams, is equal to $6.022140857 \times 10^{23}$, or roughly a 6 followed by 23 zeroes. This gives you some idea of why the statistical behaviour of matter overwhelms the individual reversible interactions to produce effects like melting ice cubes and Brownian motion.* As Einstein summarised:

> If the prediction of this motion were to be proved wrong, this fact would be a far-reaching argument against the molecular-kinetic conception of heat.

Of course it was not proved wrong, and this was taken as clinching evidence of the reality of atoms and molecules. But there's more – more even than Einstein realised in 1905.

The molecular-kinetic theory of heat that Einstein mentioned explains the division of everyday things into solid, liquid, or gaseous states. A gas is the archetypal example of atoms moving in the void, with nothing between them. A liquid is envisaged as a collection of atoms (or molecules) sliding past one another fairly freely, with no space between them. And in a solid, the particles are pictured as set firmly in an array, touching one another, again with no spaces between the atoms or molecules. So why did I describe my keyboard

---

* In case you are worried about those pool balls, in order for a set of stationary balls lying on the table to start moving together into a pack, the material of the table would have to cool down as it gave up energy to the balls, like ice giving up energy to the water in a glass. This is possible, but extremely unlikely, because of the vast number of particles in the table that would have to work together, *not* because of the relatively small number of pool balls having to work together.

and my fingers as mostly empty space? This was a really sensational discovery, and it was made by researchers in Manchester at the end of the first decade of the twentieth century, little more than a hundred years ago.

The people who actually did the experiments were Hans Geiger and Ernest Marsden, working under the supervision of Ernest Rutherford. Rutherford was one of the key figures in the development of physics around this time. He came from New Zealand, and in the 1890s worked in Cambridge, England, where he investigated the behaviour of the newly-discovered X-rays, then in 1898 moved on to McGill University in Montreal where he investigated the other great discovery of the time, radioactivity. He settled in Manchester in 1907. Within a year, his team had established that one form of this radiation, called alpha radiation, is actually a stream of particles, each one identical to a helium atom which has lost two units of negative electric charge (two electrons, we now know). Because this leaves the stripped helium atoms, also known as alpha particles, with two units of positive charge, they can be manipulated with electric and magnetic fields, steered into beams and accelerated; it's a sign of how fast physics was progressing in the first decade of the twentieth century that by 1909 the Manchester team was using alpha particles produced by natural radioactivity and manipulated in this way to probe the structure of matter.

At that time, adherents to the atomic theory thought of atoms as balls of positively charged stuff with negatively

Ernest Rutherford
Library of Congress/Science Photo Library

charged electrons embedded in the balls, like pips embedded in a watermelon or plums in a plum pudding (this model had been developed by J.J. Thomson, who had been Rutherford's mentor in his early days in Cambridge, and who is credited with the discovery of the electron). Rutherford and Geiger had been firing alpha particles through thin sheets of gold foil and monitoring how they were deflected on their journey. The alpha particles that had passed through the foil were detected on the other side using a scintillation screen, where they made little flashes of light.* Geiger had a promising student, Marsden, whom he wanted to encourage, and Rutherford suggested that he could look to see if any of the alpha particles were being reflected by the foil. Nobody expected that he would see much, if anything at all. It was the kind of boring and probably pointless job that is given to a student to provide experience in running an experiment. But to his surprise Marsden saw flashes on the detector screen at a rate of more than one a second. Many alpha particles were being reflected in some way, either deflected through a large angle to one side or bounced back nearly the way they had come. As Rutherford later remarked: 'It was as if you fired a 15-inch shell at a piece of tissue paper and it came back and hit you.' But there was no sudden flash of insight into what was going on.

Rutherford's first thought was that there might be a concentration of negative electric charge deep inside Thomson's

* This is not the famous Geiger counter, but it is the same Geiger.

'plum pudding'. This would attract the positively charged and fast-moving alpha particles and send them swinging around the negative charge and back in the direction they came from, like a comet being attracted by the gravity of the Sun and swinging round it before heading back into deep space. Then, after a continuing series of careful experiments to build up a clearer picture of what was going on, he hit on a better idea, which fitted the pattern of scintillations more closely. There must be a concentration of *positive* charge at the centre of the atom (now called the nucleus) surrounded by a much larger cloud of negative charge associated with the electrons. Most alpha particles brushed through the electron cloud and went on their way, but the relatively small number that scored a direct hit on the nucleus were reflected by its positive charge and bounced back. Using the statistics of the experiment, where one in a few thousand alpha particles were affected in this way, in 1911 Rutherford concluded that the nucleus was less than one-hundred-thousandth of the size of the atom. The discovery of the concentration of charge at the heart of the atom was announced at a scientific meeting in Manchester, and published in May 1911, although Rutherford only came down firmly in favour of a *positively* charged nucleus in 1912. The explanation of why the negatively charged electrons didn't all fall into the positively charged nucleus had to await the development of quantum theory, but from that moment on there was no doubt that the atom was mostly empty space, and it soon became clear that alpha particles are, in fact, helium nuclei.

Modern measurements have shown that the diameter of the nucleus is in the range of roughly 1.7 femtometres (1.7566 $\times 10^{-15}$m) for hydrogen (the lightest element) to about 12 fm for uranium, the heaviest naturally occurring element. The diameters of atoms range from 0.1 to 0.5 nanometres (1 $\times 10^{-10}$m to 5×10^{-10}m), so the relative sizes of atoms and nuclei are very much in line with Rutherford's early estimates.

For people unfamiliar with such small numbers, the emptiness of the atom can be pictured more graphically. If the nucleus were the size of a grain of sand, an atom would be the size of the Albert Hall. Very roughly, the difference in size between an atom and a nucleus is also comparable to the size of yourself compared with one of your cells. And for sports fans, if the nucleus were the size of a golf ball, an atom would be about 2.5 kilometres in diameter. You get the picture. It is only electric forces operating in the clouds of almost empty space surrounding tiny nuclei that make it possible for atoms to cling together to make 'solid' objects. It is also the behaviour of electrons in the clouds surrounding nuclei that makes it possible for us to work out what the stars are made of.

PILLAR

The Stars Are Suns and We Know What They Are Made Of

In 1835 the philosopher Auguste Comte wrote that 'there is no conceivable means by which we shall one day determine the chemical composition of the stars'. In 1859, a technique for determining the chemical composition of the stars was presented in a paper to the Prussian Academy of Sciences. The juxtaposition highlights what an astonishing surprise this was, although that 1859 presentation was far from being the end of the story.

The story had actually begun, unknown to Comte, in 1802, when the English physician and physicist William Hyde Wollaston was studying the spectrum made by sunlight when it is spread out by a triangular glass prism to make a rainbow pattern. He noticed that the pattern was broken up by dark lines, two in the red part of the spectrum, three in the green region, and four at the blue end. He thought these were just gaps between the colours, and didn't follow his discovery up. In 1814, the German industrial scientist Josef von Fraunhofer independently made the same discovery when he was carrying out experiments to improve the quality of the glass used in lenses and prisms. He first noticed the opposite effect from Wollaston – when the light from a flame was passed through a prism, there were two bright yellow lines in the spectrum, at very well-defined wavelengths. He used this pure yellow light to test the optical properties of different kinds of glass, and then looked at the way the glass affected sunlight. At that point, he saw the dark lines discovered, unknown to him, by Wollaston. Because he had better equipment and high-quality glass, Fraunhofer saw many more lines in the solar spectrum, eventually counting 576 of them, each at a specific wavelength; the overall effect is rather like a barcode. Significantly, he saw the same sort of pattern of lines in the light from Venus and from stars. He never found out what caused the pattern, but to this day they are known as Fraunhofer lines.

The next big step was taken by Robert Bunsen and Gustav Kirchhoff, working in Heidelberg in the 1850s. They knew, as all chemists at the time did, that different substances sprinkled into a clear flame would make it flare up with different colours – yellow for a trace of sodium (as in common salt, sodium chloride), blue-green for copper, and so on. They had a very good type of burner to use in these 'flame tests', the one named after Bunsen himself,* and built an apparatus incorporating a

* The basic burner was designed by Michael Faraday and improved by Peter Desaga, Bunsen's assistant, who marketed it under Bunsen's name.

prism and an eyepiece like that of a microscope to study the light in detail (this was the first spectroscope). When they analysed the coloured light produced in this way using spectroscopy, they found that in the heat of the flame each element produces distinctive sharp lines at specific wavelengths. The two yellow lines noticed by Fraunhofer are produced by sodium, copper makes sharp lines in the blue-green part of the spectrum, and so on. They realised that any hot object produces its own pattern of distinctive lines in the spectrum.* Then serendipity stepped in.

One evening, while they were working in their laboratory in Heidelberg a major fire broke out in Mannheim, about ten miles away. They were in the right place at the right time to analyse the light from the fire using spectroscopy, and were able to identify lines corresponding to strontium and barium in the spectrum. According to a story they repeated in different versions at different times later, a few days after the fire Bunsen and Kirchhoff were walking along the River Neckar when Bunsen said something like: 'If we can determine the nature of substances burning in Mannheim, we should be able to do the same thing for the Sun. But people would say we are mad to dream of such a thing.'

. . . .

* An explanation of *why* this happens had to await the development of quantum theory in the twentieth century; but that didn't matter to the chemists of the time.

Back in the lab, they tested the mad idea. Kirchhoff almost immediately identified the familiar double lines of sodium in the yellow part of the solar spectrum, then they found, with Kirchhoff taking the lead, that many of the dark Fraunhofer lines occurred at wavelengths where specific elements produce bright lines when heated in the flame of a Bunsen burner. The implication is that although hot things produce bright lines in the spectrum, when light passes through cool things they absorb light at the corresponding wavelengths, making dark lines. Light from the hot interior of the Sun must be passing through cooler outer layers to produce this effect. It *was* possible to determine what the Sun was made of. Kirchhoff was so astonished that he exclaimed, referring back to their riverside conversation, 'Bunsen, I have gone mad!' Bunsen replied, 'So have I, Kirchhoff.' It was this work that formed the basis of Kirchhoff's presentation to the Prussian Academy on 27 October 1859. It really was possible to say what the Sun and stars were made of. Or was it?

At first, everything looked good. The great triumph of the new technique for analysing light from stars came following an eclipse of the Sun visible from India on 18 August 1868 – the first eclipse following Kirchhoff's realisation that Fraunhofer lines are caused by specific elements blocking light from the Sun at particular wavelengths. During an eclipse, with the light from the main disc of the Sun blocked out by the Moon, it is possible to study the fainter light from regions just above the surface. The French astronomer Pierre Janssen did just that, and found a very bright yellow line close to the expected sodium lines. This feature was so bright that he realised he could still study it even after the eclipse, and he made more observations before returning to France. Meanwhile, an English astronomer, Norman Lockyer, had developed a new spectroscope that he used to study light from the outer regions of the Sun on 20 October 1868. He found the same yellow line. Janssen and Lockyer were both credited with the discovery. But it was Lockyer alone who took the bold step of claiming that the line must be produced by an element that was unknown on Earth, and gave it the name helium, from the Greek word for the Sun. The suggestion remained controversial until 1895, when William Ramsay found that a gas released by uranium (we now know, as a result of radioactive decay) produces the same bright yellow line in the spectrum. An element had actually been 'found' in the Sun 27 years before it was found on Earth. At the beginning of the twentieth century, the plethora of elements identified by spectroscopy seemed to be telling us that although the Sun was being kept hot by some unknown process, its composition was very much like that of the Earth. But this interpretation of the evidence was wrong. There were still surprises in store.

Although the interpretation was wrong, it was based on what seemed to be solid evidence. At the end of the nineteenth century, the state of knowledge about the Sun's composition was summed up by Henry Rowland in a series of tables identifying 36 elements and giving details of the strength of their spectral lines. This information revealed the relative proportions of these elements – how many atoms of oxygen for each atom of carbon, and so on – which matched the proportions seen on Earth. Largely as a result of Rowland's work, the idea that the Sun's composition was much the same as that of the Earth persisted for a quarter of a century. Then came the first surprise.

In 1924 Cecilia Payne was working for a PhD at Harvard University. Payne was English, and had studied at Newnham College in Cambridge, but had not been allowed to take a degree there, let alone a PhD, because she was a woman. That was why she had moved to America, where in 1925 she would be the first woman to be awarded a PhD by Radcliffe College, based on her work at Harvard College Observatory. This was just the beginning of a glittering career,* but nothing surpassed what she achieved in the mid-1920s. Her starting point was recent work by the Indian physicist Meghnad Saha which had explained how details of the Fraunhofer lines were affected by the physical conditions (temperature, pressure and so on) in different parts of a star. Armed with this information, she was able to work out the proportions of eighteen elements in several stars more accurately than anyone before her, showing that they were essentially the same for all stars once allowance was made for these effects. Most of these abundances were in line with Rowland's tables for the solar abundances.

....

* Mostly carried out under her married name, Cecilia Payne-Gaposchkin.

Cecilia Payne-Gaposchkin
Smithsonian Institution/Science Photo Library

But there was one dramatic difference. According to Payne's calculations, there was overwhelmingly more hydrogen and helium in the stars than everything else put together.

When Payne prepared the draft of her thesis, including this discovery, her supervisor, Harlow Shapley, sent it to be reviewed by Henry Norris Russell, a senior astronomer at Princeton. He said that this result was 'clearly impossible'. Back in 1914, in an article on 'The Solar Spectrum and the Earth's Crust', Russell had written:

> The agreement of the solar and terrestrial lists is such as to confirm very strongly Rowland's opinion that, if the Earth's crust should be raised to the temperature of the Sun's atmosphere, it would give a very similar absorption spectrum. The spectra of the Sun and other stars were similar, so it appeared that the relative abundance of elements in the universe was like that in Earth's crust.[4]

And he still held to that view. On Shapley's advice, when Payne formally submitted her thesis in 1925 she included the sentence 'the enormous abundances derived for [hydrogen and helium] in the stellar atmospheres is almost certainly not real'.

But this was an idea whose time had come. In 1928 the astronomer Albrecht Unsöld, working in Göttingen, made a study of the solar spectrum, and came to the conclusion that the atmosphere of the Sun must be mostly composed of hydrogen. A young Irish research student, William McCrea, was visiting Göttingen at the time, and developed this suggestion with a calculation that showed there were a million times more hydrogen atoms in the solar atmosphere than the amount of everything else, except helium, put together.* His PhD, for a thesis on 'Problems Concerning the Outer Layers of the Sun', was awarded by Cambridge University in 1929. About the same time, Russell was changing his mind about the impossibility of Payne's results. Building from Unsöld's work, and also using the Saha equations, Russell carried out a detailed study of the solar spectrum, which provided relative abundances for 56 elements. This was the best set of data yet on the Sun's composition, including evidence that 'the great abundance of hydrogen can hardly be doubted', even though he described it as 'almost incredibly great'. Russell was careful to give full credit to Payne when he published his own work, but because he was already an established scientist his paper made a big splash at the time, and he often received her share of the credit for the discovery. His work did go further than hers, but hers did come first; in 1962, the astronomer Otto Struve described her thesis as 'the most brilliant PhD thesis ever written in astronomy' up to that time. What had been 'impossible' in 1925 was merely 'almost' incredible in 1929.

But there was still more to surprise astronomers, hinted at in Russell's comment in 1914 that 'it appeared that the relative

---

* Much later, McCrea was my supervisor when I studied astronomy at the University of Sussex, but his brilliance did not rub off on me!

abundance of elements in the universe was like that in Earth's crust'. If the stars were not made of the same elements in the same abundances as the Earth's crust, then the composition of the Universe is not like that of the Earth's crust. Specifically, the Universe must contain a lot more hydrogen and helium. Just how much more only became clear nearly three decades after the pioneering work of Payne, Unsöld, McCrea and Russell.

By the end of the 1920s, astronomers had a surprisingly good understanding of the nature of a star like the Sun, even though they did not know the exact details of how it generated heat in its interior. A star is basically a ball of hot gas which is balancing two opposing forces to maintain equilibrium. Gravity is trying to pull the ball together and make it shrink, while the pressure generated by the heat in its interior is pushing outwards to hold it up. Astronomers can calculate the mass of the Sun by studying the orbits of the planets, held in place by the Sun's gravity, so they know how strong the inward force is. Because of the equilibrium, this means they know how strong the outward force is, which tells them about the conditions inside the Sun, including the temperature at its core. The details were worked out by the pioneering astrophysicist Arthur Eddington, and published in a book, *The Internal Constitution of the Stars*, in 1926. By then, thanks to Albert Einstein, physicists knew that energy could be released by nuclear fusion. A great deal of energy could be released in this way if four hydrogen nuclei (single protons) could be converted into one helium nucleus (alpha particles, each composed of two protons and two neutrons bound together), because each helium nucleus has less mass than the combined mass of four individual protons. The energy released in each such fusion is equal to this 'lost' mass multiplied by the square of the speed of light. Even before astronomers realised just how much hydrogen the Sun and stars contain, all potentially available to be involved in this process, Eddington proposed that their heat is generated in this way since 'the helium which we handle must have been put together at some time and some place'. The question was, how?

The search for an answer to the question was handicapped by an unfortunate coincidence. In the 1930s, astrophysicists developed more detailed 'models' (sets of equations describing what was going on) of stellar interiors. They found that the pressure which holds a star up has two parts. One is the regular process we think of as pressure, with particles bouncing around and colliding with one another, like the molecules of air in a balloon. But the interior of a star is so hot that negatively charged electrons are stripped from positively charged nuclei. The resulting sea of charged particles interacts with the electromagnetic radiation – light, X-rays and so on – released at the heart of the star and making its way to the surface. This produces an additional outward force, known as radiation pressure. A star like the Sun is stable when the combination of both these kinds of pressure balances the inward tug of gravity. But it turns out there are two ways to achieve this balance.

The conventional pressure depends on the number of particles there are. Electrons are so much lighter than protons and neutrons that they can be ignored for this purpose, so what matters is the number of atomic nuclei. But the radiation pressure does depend on the number of electrons. A hydrogen atom only has one electron, so it can only contribute one electron per nucleus, but a helium atom has two electrons, so it can contribute two electrons per nucleus, and so on. So the proportions of the overall pressure contributed by conventional pressure and by radiation pressure depend on how many nuclei of heavy elements there are in the mix. The unfortunate coincidence is that for a star with the mass and brightness of the Sun, or any similar star, the inward tug of gravity can be balanced by a combination of the two pressures *either* if at least 95 per cent of the star is composed of a mixture of hydrogen and helium, *or* if there is just 35 per cent light stuff and 65 per cent heavier elements. In the 1930s, having only just realised that stars are not made entirely of heavier elements, astronomers leaned towards the second option. To accept that elements like those we find on Earth made up no more than 5 per cent of the Sun and stars was too big a leap for them to accept.

So the first attempts to explain how energy is generated in stars – how hydrogen nuclei are combined to make helium nuclei – had the assumption of 35 per cent hydrogen built in to them. This misunderstanding affected the work of the first people to attempt to explain the process, initially carried out by Fritz Houtermans and Robert Atkinson in collaboration and then developed by Atkinson. The essence of this idea is that heavier nuclei absorb four protons one after another, and then spit out alpha particles – helium nuclei. It turns out that this process is important in some stars a bit more massive than the Sun, but the process which actually releases energy inside the Sun is much simpler. This starts with two protons getting together and spitting out a positron (a positively charged counterpart to the electron) to make a deuteron, a nucleus consisting of a single proton and a single neutron bound together. The addition of another proton makes a nucleus of helium-3, and when two helium-3 nuclei interact they form a nucleus of helium-4 (two protons and two neutrons, an alpha particle) with two protons being ejected. The net effect is that four hydrogen nuclei have been converted into one helium nucleus, and energy has been released. The essence of this 'proton-proton chain' was worked out by Charles Critchfield in 1938, but it was only fully understood, with the implication that the Sun is at least 95 per cent made of hydrogen and helium, in the 1950s.

You need a lot of hydrogen to make this work, because the chances of any two hydrogen nuclei bumping into one another with enough force to make a deuteron, even under the extreme conditions at the heart of the Sun, are small. Modern calculations, greatly aided by the advent of high-speed electronic computers, tell us that it would take an individual proton, bouncing around in the heart of the Sun where the temperature is about 15 million degrees Celsius, 14 billion years before it was involved in a head-on collision with a partner to form a deuteron. Some take longer, some take less time, but statistically speaking just one collision in every 10 billion trillion will trigger the start of the proton-proton chain. And the other steps in the chain are comparably unlikely. Each time four protons are converted into a single helium nucleus, just 0.7 per cent of the mass is converted into energy. Yet in spite of the rarity of these events and the small amount of mass-energy released each time, overall the Sun is converting 5 million tonnes of mass (the equivalent of a million medium-sized African elephants) into energy every second, as 616 million tonnes of hydrogen is converted into 611 million tonnes of helium. It has been doing this for 4.5 billion years, but it started out with so much hydrogen that so far it has processed only about 4 per cent of its hydrogen fuel into helium ash.

As far as the composition of the Sun (and similar stars) is concerned, the situation is even more extreme than the simple calculations carried out in the 1930s suggested. They said that *at least* 95 per cent of the Sun must be in the form of hydrogen and helium. We now know, from a combination of observations and computer modelling, that in terms of mass the Sun is made up of some 71 per cent hydrogen, roughly 27 per cent helium, and less than 2 per cent of everything else put together. In terms of the number of atoms (nuclei) the numbers are even more impressive. Hydrogen nuclei make up

91.2 per cent of the Sun, helium 8.7 per cent, and everything else just 0.1 per cent. These numbers apply to the proportions of the chemical elements in stars across the Universe, and planets are insignificant (in cosmic terms) specks of dust compared with their parent stars (the Sun is as big as 1.3 million Earth-sized planets put together). Everything that matters to us is part of the 2 per cent, or 0.1 per cent if you are counting atoms, a kind of afterthought of creation. This was one of the biggest surprises of science. Yet, arguably even more surprisingly, that 2 per cent has produced life, including ourselves. How it has done so forms one of the other pillars of science.

PILLAR

There is No Life Force

The idea that life is special – that living things are powered by a mysterious 'life force' that inanimate objects lack – is older than history, and was discussed by the philosophers of ancient Egypt and Greece. It seems like common sense. But as so often with our understanding of the world, common sense is a bad guide to reality.

The beginning of a proper understanding of how living things work came with experiments carried out by the French chemist Antoine Lavoisier and his colleague Pierre Laplace in the 1780s. They put a guinea pig in a container which stood inside another container packed with ice, and measured how much ice was melted by the animal's body heat in a certain time. They also measured how much 'fixed air' (now known as carbon dioxide) the animal breathed out. They found that this was the same as the amount produced by burning charcoal to melt the same amount of ice. Animals were seen to obey the same laws as burning charcoal, or candles.

In the following decade, though, another discovery seemed

to suggest at first that there really is a life force. Famously, the Italian physician Luigi Galvani accidentally discovered that a pair of frog's legs that had been dissected twitched when they were in contact with iron. The story is a little more complicated than many popular accounts suggest, though, and it is worth going over the details to see how a scientist's mind works.

Galvani carried out many kinds of experiments, and in his lab there was a hand-cranked machine which generated static electricity through friction, like the shock you can get when touching a metal object after walking across some kinds of carpet. One day he was dissecting a pair of frog's legs, using a scalpel which had touched the machine and picked up an electric charge. When the scalpel touched the sciatic nerve of one of the legs, the leg kicked as if it were still alive. This led him to experiments which showed that legs from a dead frog would twitch if they were connected directly to the electrical machine, or if they were laid out on a metal sheet during a thunderstorm, when there was lightning in the air. But his key observation came about by accident. When he was getting the sets of legs ready for his experiments, Galvani would hang them up to dry on brass hooks in the open air. One of these hooks touched an iron fence, and the legs kicked, although there was no outside source of electricity. When he took the legs and hook inside, keeping them well away from his electrical machine, and touched the hook onto iron, the legs twitched again. It happened every time, with every set of legs.

He believed that this proved the presence of some kind of 'animal electricity', different from the 'static' electricity that makes lightning, or that we can make by friction. This animal electricity was supposed to be a kind of fluid, manufactured in the brain, which was carried to the muscles by nerves, and stored there until needed. Galvani's compatriot, Alessandro Volta, disagreed. He said that the electricity that produced the twitching was not something to do with a life force, but the result of an interaction involving the metals the dissected legs were touching. This led him, through a series of experiments, to invent a device for making electricity. It was a pile of alternating silver and zinc discs, separated by cardboard discs soaked in brine. When the top of the pile was connected to the bottom by a wire, an electric current flowed in the wire. The 'Voltaic pile' was the first electric battery.

Volta's invention was developed at the Royal Institution in London and applied there by Humphry Davy in dramatic experiments that used electricity to break down compounds into their constituent parts, revealing the existence of 'new' metals, including potassium and sodium. But instead of quashing the idea of a life force, Davy's experiments encouraged some supporters of the idea. In particular, a London-based surgeon, John Abernethy, saw a link between electricity and something he called Vitality – essentially his name for the life force. His conclusions were attacked by one of his colleagues, William Lawrence, triggering a debate that raged in the second decade of the nineteenth century (it is no coincidence that Mary Shelley wrote her novel *Frankenstein* just at this time; Lawrence was Percy Bysshe Shelley's doctor from 1815 to 1818). The study of electricity could not settle the issue. But the surprising result of a chemical experiment carried out in 1828 should have laid vitalism to rest.

By the end of the eighteenth century, chemists were beginning to get a handle on how different substances combined to form more complicated compounds. It was soon clear that carbon can indeed form a great variety of complicated combinations with other things, and that living things are largely made up of such complicated carbon compounds. The chemistry of such carbon compounds became known as organic chemistry, regarded as something distinct from the chemistry of ordinary 'inorganic' things like water, and was associated with the idea of vitalism. Organic compounds, it was thought, could only be manufactured by living things, thanks to the power of the life force.

In 1773, Hilaire Rouelle, a French chemist, had isolated crystals of a previously unknown substance from the urine of various animals, including people. This became known as urea, and it was something of a puzzle because even at the time it was clear that it is a relatively simple compound (its modern formula is $H_2N\text{-}CO\text{-}NH_2$). It didn't really seem complicated enough to require the influence of a life force in its manufacture. As it turned out, it wasn't.

In 1828, the German chemist Friedrich Wöhler was trying to make ammonium cyanate by reacting cyanic acid with ammonia. The stuff produced by his experiment, however, was not ammonium cyanate. Careful analysis showed him that it was urea, identical to the stuff extracted from urine. His surprise was expressed in the introduction to the paper he wrote reporting the discovery, in 1828:

> This investigation gave the unexpected result that by combining cyanic acid and ammonia urea is generated. Quite a peculiar fact in that it represents the artificial (in vitro) formation of an organic compound, so-called 'animalischem Stoff', out of inorganic compounds.

He was less formal in a letter he wrote that year to a colleague, Jacob Berzelius, to inform him that he [Wöhler]:

> is capable of producing urea requiring neither kidneys nor any animal, may it be man or dog. Ammonium cyanate is urea … it is by no chemical means different from urea of the urine, which I have produced all by myself.

This might have been something of a killer blow to the idea of a life force. But one reason why it did not have the immediate impact that we might expect with hindsight is revealed in the quote from that letter. Wöhler's tests showed that chemically speaking, urea and ammonium cyanate are identical. A molecule of ammonium cyanate does actually contain the same atoms as a molecule of urea, but in a different geometrical arrangement. Such non-identical twin molecules are now known as isomers, and Wöhler was much more interested in following up the discovery of isomerism than in getting involved in the vitalism debate. Besides, urea is a relatively simple substance, and supporters of the idea of a special kind of chemistry of life could (and did) argue that it hardly counted as an organic molecule at all. There were many other organic molecules that were more complicated and could not be synthesised.

The only way to lay vitalism to rest was to synthesise a lot more of these complicated organic molecules, starting from simple inorganic molecules – a process known as 'total synthesis'. Wöhler's discovery had been a happy accident, a stroke of serendipity. But in 1845 another German, Adolph Kolbe, deliberately set out to make organic compounds from inorganic substances. He gave himself the task of converting carbon disulphide, an inorganic compound easily made out of its constituent parts, into acetic acid, or vinegar, an organic compound produced naturally by fermentation. Kolbe's success was the second complete synthesis of an organic compound from inorganic precursors, without involving any biological processes. But even two examples left a lot of organic molecules to be investigated.

In the 1850s, the Parisian Marcellin Berthelot, an almost evangelical opponent of vitalism, set out to use total synthesis to manufacture every organic molecule known at the time. His conviction was that all chemical processes are based on the

Marcellin Berthelot
Science Photo Library

action of physical forces which can be studied and measured like the forces involved in mechanical processes. His programme of total synthesis of every organic substance followed logically from that conviction; it was an impossible dream, but he did enough to show that he was right.

Berthelot planned a step-by-step approach. He started out with simple compounds containing carbon and hydrogen (hydrocarbons, such as methane), converted them to alcohols (which contain an OH group, essentially water with one hydrogen atom missing, so it can link to other things), then changed them into esters (where the OH group is replaced by a more complex 'alkoxy' group), converted them into organic acids (which contain even more complex groups) and so on. Berthelot had many successes. He was able to make formic acid (the chemical ants use to sting with) using the step-by-step approach just outlined, acetylene (which he named) by sparking an electric arc between carbon electrodes in an atmosphere of hydrogen, and benzene by heating acetylene in a glass tube.

Benzene was a crucial step. Each molecule of benzene is built upon six carbon atoms joined in a ring. Benzene is found naturally in crude oil, which is the remains of living organisms, and these ring molecules, which are integral components in a huge variety of compounds, are particularly important in the chemistry of life. The branch of chemistry involving the reactions of such ring molecules is now known as aromatics.

Berthelot's epic programme of total synthesis was far too ambitious for one man to complete, but he established something which is now one of the pillars of science. He showed that it is possible to manufacture organic substances from four elements that are found in all living things – carbon, hydrogen, oxygen and nitrogen. These are so important, and so often (always!) found together in organic material, that they are collectively referred to as CHON. Berthelot's opus on the synthesis of organic chemicals, *Chimie organique fondée sur la synthèse*, was published in 1860. It should have sounded the death knell of vitalism. But the idea that living things, including ourselves, are nothing more than collections of carbon compounds which operate through the action of physical forces like the forces involved in mechanical processes was so hard to stomach – so counter to 'common sense' – that even at the end of the nineteenth century the idea that there was something special about the chemistry of life, and that some 'life force' was involved in what were called vitalistic processes, was still a subject for debate. As respectable a scientist as Louis Pasteur argued in its favour. The final refutation of this idea came in 1897, from the work of the German Eduard Buchner.

One of the last puzzles that gave ammunition for the vitalists was fermentation. Fermentation converts foods such as sugar into simpler compounds such as alcohol and carbon dioxide, and releases energy which powers living cells. But did it always involve living cells? Buchner tackled the question using alcohol production, which involves yeast, a living organism. Yeast is essential for this process; but Buchner wanted to test whether this was because the yeast cells were alive, or because they contained some chemical substance (a catalyst) which encouraged the conversion of sugar into alcohol and carbon dioxide by inorganic reactions.

Buchner started with living yeast cells, then subjected them to a series of indignities which killed them and reduced them to their constituent chemical parts. Dry yeast cells were mixed with quartz sand and a soft crumbly rock, then ground up with a pestle and mortar. The mixture became damp as the yeast cells burst and released their contents. The damp mixture was then squeezed to extract a 'press juice' used in the experiments.

When sugar solution was mixed in to the freshly pressed yeast juice, bubbles of gas were produced, eventually covering the liquid with froth. Chemical tests showed that carbon dioxide and alcohol were being produced in exactly the same proportions as in fermentation with live yeast. But there were no living yeast cells in the extract.

Following up this work, Buchner found that the key chemical substance involved is an enzyme, which he called zymase. Zymase is manufactured inside yeast cells, so in that sense life is involved in the process of fermentation, but the key point is that zymase itself is an inanimate chemical substance, and fermentation occurs whether the yeast is alive or dead. Enzymes are crucial players in many biological processes, but it is now possible to synthesise enzymes chemically without biology being involved. As Buchner later put it:

The difference between enzymes and micro-organisms is clearly revealed when the latter are represented as the producers of the former, which we must conceive as complicated but inanimate chemical substances.

Zymase is, indeed, one of the enzymes that it is now possible to synthesise without biology being involved. But the essential point, worth reiterating, is that the chemistry carries on whether the yeast is alive or dead. In January 1897 Buchner sent his key scientific paper, *Alkoholische Gährung ohne Hefezellen* (*On alcoholic fermentation without yeast cells*), to the journal *Berichte der Deutschen Chemischen Gesellschaft*.

Buchner was awarded the Nobel Prize for chemistry in 1907, 'for his biochemical researches and his discovery of cell-free fermentation'. This is as good a date as any to choose to mark the death of vitalism. But this left another question. If there is no life force, how did life originate?

Charles Darwin thought hard about this puzzle, and speculated that life might have got started in a 'warm little pond' on Earth laced with the right chemical ingredients. But he realised that this could not happen today. As he wrote to Joseph Hooker in 1871:

It is often said that all the conditions for the first production of a living organism are now present, which could ever have been present.—But if (& oh what a big if) we could conceive in some warm little pond with all sorts of ammonia

& phosphoric salts,—light, heat, electricity &c present, that a protein compound was chemically formed, ready to undergo still more complex changes, at the present day such matter w^d be instantly devoured, or absorbed, which would not have been the case before living creatures were formed.

Half a century after Darwin wrote those words, Alexander Oparin, a Russian biochemist who had been born in 1894 and graduated from Moscow State University in 1917, the year of the Russian Revolution, put this kind of speculation onto a proper scientific footing. It was actually in 1922, at a meeting of the Russian Botanical Society, that he first aired his ideas, which he developed into a book, *The Origin of Life*, published in 1924. What stimulated his thinking was the recent discovery (thanks to spectroscopy; none of the scientific pillars stand alone!) that the atmospheres of Jupiter and the other giant planets of our Solar System contain a great amount of gases such as methane, the kind of thing Darwin (among others) envisaged as the feedstock for life. The atmosphere of the Earth today is rich in oxygen, which is very reactive. It is produced by life, but if it were not being constantly replenished it would all get used up in forest fires, weathering of rocks, and other processes. Oparin suggested that in order for life to have got started in some warm little pond, when the Earth was young its atmosphere must have been like those of the giant planets. Such a 'reducing' atmosphere might have contained methane, ammonia, water vapour, and hydrogen, and might build up organic molecules step by step, as in Berthelot's experiments. But it would have had no oxygen, which would have reacted with and destroyed the precursors of life.

Oparin's argument has been summed up in a few steps:

- There is no fundamental difference between living things and lifeless matter. The complexities of life must have developed in the process of the evolution of matter.
- The infant Earth possessed a strongly reducing atmosphere, containing methane, ammonia, hydrogen and water vapour, which were the raw materials for the evolution of life.
- As molecules got larger and more complex, their behaviour also became more complex, with interactions between molecules determined by the shape of the molecules and the way they fitted together.
- Even at this early stage, development of new structures was governed by competition, a struggle for existence as complex structures 'fed' off simpler molecules, and Darwinian natural selection.
- Living organisms are open systems, which take in energy and raw materials from outside, so they are not restricted by the second law of thermodynamics.

The last point is an important one which is often overlooked. The second law of thermodynamics is famous as the law of nature which tells us that things wear out and the amount of disorder in the world (measured in terms of a quantity called entropy) always increases. The standard example is a drinking glass that falls off a table and shatters on the floor. The shattered glass is more disordered than the original drinking vessel; entropy has increased. And you never see fragments of broken glass on the floor spontaneously rearrange themselves into a drinking vessel – negative entropy. But life seems to get around this law. Somehow, life creates order out of chaos, reversing the flow of entropy. But it can only do so on a local basis. Just as making a drinking glass requires an input of energy, so making living things and maintaining life requires an input of energy. For animals like ourselves, this comes from our food – ultimately from plants, since even if we eat meat, the meat comes from animals that ate plants. For plants the energy comes ultimately from sunlight. The living Earth is like a bubble of reversed entropy flow, all feeding off the energy stream flowing out from the Sun. And that is more than compensated for by the vast increase in entropy that is associated with the processes that keep the Sun shining.

Oparin's specific suggestion was that with the aid of energy from sunlight or some other outside source, such as lightning, in the kind of reducing atmosphere he envisaged, entropy could have 'run backwards' to build up complex molecules containing carbon – organic molecules. Such things could grow into sheets and tiny droplets or even little hollow bubbles, the sort of thing that might develop into cells. Oparin's work went largely unnoticed outside his homeland at the time, but as if to show that the time was indeed ripe for it, the British researcher J.B.S. Haldane independently came up with what was essentially the same idea in 1929. And it was Haldane (who, as we saw earlier, had a gift for memorable scientific quips) who thought up a catchy name for the hypothetical 'warm little pond' in which all of this took place – the primordial soup. The next step was to try to create, or recreate, the conditions that existed in the primordial soup in the laboratory. But although those experiments were successful up to a point, they raised new questions, and were overtaken by another surprise, which has itself become one of the pillars of science.

PILLAR

The Milky Way is a Warehouse Stocked with the Raw Ingredients of Life

Two decades after Oparin suggested that life might have originated under a reducing atmosphere on the early Earth, Harold Urey, a chemistry professor at the University of Chicago, gave his students a lecture about what he referred to as 'the Oparin-Haldane hypothesis'. One of those students, a recent graduate named Stanley Miller, was sufficiently intrigued to ask if he could work for his doctorate by building an experiment to test the idea – a 'warm little pond' in miniature sealed within the glass vessels of a laboratory and containing the mixture of materials suggested by Oparin and Haldane.

Urey agreed to supervise the work, and the result became famous as the Miller–Urey experiment.

The centrepiece of the experiment was a 5-litre glass flask which held a mixture of methane, ammonia, water vapour, and hydrogen. The water vapour was provided continuously from a second half-litre flask of boiling water linked to the

Stanley Miller
Science Photo Library

main flask by tubes; the vapour passed through the main flask and then condensed, with the hot gases from the larger flask continuing through a cooling chamber, shaped like a U-bend, and going back to the boiling flask to complete the loop. The U-bend provided a trap in which liquid could be caught and drained off through a tap. To provide energy by mimicking the action of lightning, electric sparks flashed through the mixture in the main flask.

In the original form of the experiment, the liquid trapped in the U-bend was drained off and analysed once a week. But it didn't take more than a single week for the experiment to prove a spectacular success, with results well worth the award of a PhD. In less than a day, the liquid in the U-bend had turned pink. When the first week's worth of liquid was drained off and analysed, Miller found that more than 10 per cent of the carbon from the original mixture of gases sealed into the 5-litre flask had been converted into organic compounds. The most important of these were amino acids, complex organic molecules which are themselves the components of proteins, the building blocks of life. There are just twenty amino acids which combine with one another in different ways to form all the proteins in your body. The Miller–Urey experiment had made thirteen of them in just a week. The results were published in the journal *Science* in 1953. They were seen as being just one step short of making life itself, and Miller dedicated his entire scientific career (he died in 2007) to refining his experiment and improving it, with longer and longer runs, in the hope of taking that extra step. He was undaunted when the geologists decided that the Earth had probably not started out with a reducing atmosphere at all. The best evidence is that the early atmosphere of our planet was composed of the same mixture of gases that spews from volcanoes today – carbon dioxide, nitrogen and sulphur dioxide prominent among them. Miller simply adapted his apparatus to accommodate this mixture of materials and tried again, once again producing a wide variety of complex organic molecules from the simple feedstock. If nothing else, he established that provided there is an input of energy it is not only easy but inevitable that molecules as complex as amino acids will be built up from simple compounds. Ironically, though, he needn't have bothered trying to explain how such molecules arrived on Earth. The big surprise stemming from observations made at the end of the twentieth century and into the early twenty-first century, shaking up our understanding of the origin of life on Earth, is that the chemistry of the warm little ponds on the young Earth may have *started* with compounds like amino acids.

We have moved on a long way since the pioneering work of the nineteenth-century biochemists. If one of their heirs today wanted to manufacture the fundamental molecules of life, proteins and the famous nucleic acids DNA and RNA, he or she wouldn't bother starting out from the mixture of gases that might have been found in a reducing atmosphere, or even from the mixture of gases belched out by volcanoes today.* Much more complex and interesting feedstock, things like formaldehyde and methanol, is available from chemical suppliers, and is probably on the shelves of any decent biochemical lab. Of course, the reason it is so readily available is that someone else has gone to the trouble of manufacturing it by total synthesis, on an industrial scale. The bombshell is that the Universe has done the same thing, on a vastly bigger scale and for a large number of the precursors of life.

The story starts in the 1930s, when simplest molecular compounds of carbon and hydrogen (CH) and carbon and nitrogen (CN) were found in clouds of gas and dust in space (nebulae) using spectroscopy. But the story only began to get interesting in the 1960s, when new technology extended the range of wavelengths that could be investigated in this way. Small molecules, like those first two to be identified in space, produce lines in the visible part of the spectrum. But larger molecules produce equivalent features in the spectrum at longer wavelengths, in the infrared and radio parts of the spectrum. So their identification had to await the development of suitable technology, in the form of infrared and radio telescopes, to make the appropriate identifications. Even then, since nobody expected to find complex molecules in space

....

* To my surprise, after I had written this section, in the autumn of 2019 researchers based at Ludwig Maximilian University of Munich in Germany reported results of recent laboratory experiments in which complex organic molecules were built up from ingredients such as water and nitrogen. Some people are gluttons for punishment.

it took a while for astronomers to realise what it was they were seeing. Then the penny dropped, and they began actively searching for molecules in space, seeking out bigger and more complex varieties in a competition to find the one with the most atoms linked together.

The third molecule found in space was the so-called hydroxyl radical, OH, identified in 1963. But it was the next discovery, made in 1968, that made people begin to sit up and take notice. This was the four-atom molecule ammonia, NH_3. It was the first indication that more than two atoms could get together under the conditions of interstellar space to make molecules. Water (H_2O) was one of the first three-atom molecules to be identified, but much more excitement was stirred by the discovery of formaldehyde (H_2CO), the first organic molecule found in space. A couple of hundred interstellar molecules have now been identified, including urea* and ethyl alcohol. The discovery of ethyl alcohol was particularly interesting, not just because it gave headline writers in popular papers an opportunity to refer to clouds of 'vodka in space' but because each molecule is made up of nine atoms, CH_3CH_2OH. There are a few definitely identified molecules with ten or more atoms each, but one that is particularly intriguing is glycine, H_2NH_2CCOOH. Glycine is an amino acid, one of the building blocks of proteins. What Miller could do in a 5-litre

---

* Detected in 2014 and definitely manufactured in interstellar clouds without the use of kidneys, either man or dog.

flask in his lab the Universe can do in vast clouds of gas in space.

Another significant discovery is a twelve-atom molecule called iso-propyl cyanide, $(CH_3)_2CHCN$, identified in 2014. This is significant because the notation $(CH_3)_2$ means that two separate CH_3 units branch off from the same carbon atom; this is a structure similar to that of many of the complex molecules of life found on Earth, including some of the amino acids. Two years later, in 2016, astronomers detected the ten-atom molecule propylene oxide, CH_3CHCH_2O in a cloud of gas and dust called Sagittarius B2. The specially interesting feature of this molecule is that it has a property called chirality, which is essentially handedness. It comes naturally in left-handed and right-handed varieties – but only one kind was found in 2016. Helices have chirality – they can twist either to the left or to the right. Life on Earth is neatly divided into both kinds of chirality. Amino acids are almost entirely left-handed, while the helices of RNA and DNA are right-handed. The propylene oxide seen in clouds like Sagittarius B2 will have their chirality determined by the action of light* from stars which only allows one kind of handedness to be imprinted on the molecules within an individual cloud of gas and dust, although the observations aren't yet detailed enough to pick out which handedness dominates in this case. Since stars and planets form from such clouds, the implication is that the handedness

....

* For the technically minded, circularly polarised light.

is imprinted on the components of life before they even reach the surface of a planet. All the planetary systems that form from the same cloud should have the same handedness. But how exactly do these molecules form in space, and how can they reach the surface of a planet?

Mention of 'dust' in interstellar clouds might not conjure up quite the right image in your mind. Studies of the electromagnetic radiation from these clouds across a wide range of wavelengths show that the dust is made up of tiny particles, like the particles in cigarette smoke. The particles are made of things like carbon and the oxides of silicon, and they are covered in ices made of frozen ammonia and methane, as well as familiar water ice. If two atoms, or two small molecules, or one large molecule and one small molecule, collide in space, they will most probably bounce off one another or be broken apart by the collision. But the icy surfaces of dust grains provide places where atoms and molecules can stick. When simple substances stick onto the ice they have an opportunity to join together to make more complex substances which later escape from the ice, perhaps when the grains themselves are involved in collisions, or as a result of the impact of cosmic rays, fast-moving particles ejected by stellar activity. These ideas have been tested in the lab, where icy particles like the ones that exist in space have been cooled to −263°C to mimic the cold of space and bathed in ultraviolet light to mimic the energy provided by stars. Chemical reactions take place on the surfaces of the grains in just the way I have described.

This is not a very quick process. It takes a long time to build up molecules as complex as glycine or iso-propyl cyanide. But there has been plenty of time. The Universe is about 13.8 billion years old, and our Milky Way galaxy is only a little younger. Even the Solar System and the Earth itself are around 4.5 billion years old. Fossil remains show that single-celled life forms existed on Earth at least 3.8 billion years ago, and it is a puzzle how things like carbon dioxide, water and sulphur dioxide could produce such life forms in such a short time, starting from scratch. But it is much less of a puzzle how such feedstock, plus methane and ammonia, could produce things like glycine or iso-propyl cyanide in ten or more billion years, more than twice the present age of the Earth.

How much complex organic material might there be out there? Our Milky Way contains several hundred million stars more or less like our Sun, and a variety of astronomical observations suggest that the mass of all the gas and dust between the stars is about 10 per cent of the mass of all the stars. That means at least 10 million times the mass of the Sun. And we can see what happens when such clouds of gas and dust are pulled together by gravity to make new stars and planets.

There is a system known as IRS 46, where a huge dusty disc of material surrounds a young star. This is similar to the cloud of material from which the Earth and other planets are thought to have formed around the young Sun, and it can be studied in detail because it is relatively close to us – a mere 375 light years away. The disc contains high concentrations of hydrogen cyanide and acetylene. When these two compounds, plus water, are used in laboratory experiments mimicking space conditions, they react to produce amino acids. And in 2019, NASA scientists announced that analysis of data from the Cassini space probe showed the presence of similar building blocks of life in active vents spewing water up from the ice-covered oceans of Enceladus, one of the moons of Saturn. These get their energy from hydrothermal sources deep beneath the ice. Powerful hydrothermal vents eject material from the moon's core; this mixes with water from the moon's huge ice-covered ocean before it is released into space through great geysers bursting through the ice as water vapour and ice grains. The molecules condense onto ice grains, where the detectors on Cassini showed them to be nitrogen- and oxygen-bearing compounds like those seen in the dusty discs around young stars. As Stanley Miller proved in the course of his long career, provided there is an input of energy it is not only easy but inevitable that molecules as complex as amino acids will be built up from simple compounds.

As the building blocks of proteins, amino acids are half of the story of life. The other half concerns the nucleic acids, DNA and RNA. These have not yet been detected in space. But once again, their building blocks have.

The core component of both nucleic acids is a sugar called ribose. Ribose molecules are each built around a ring of five atoms, four carbon atoms and one oxygen atom, which can link up with other things outside the ring. In ribose, three of the carbon atoms are each linked to one hydrogen atom and one OH group outside the ring. But in deoxyribose, one of the three carbon atoms is attached just to two hydrogen atoms, so that the molecule has one less oxygen atom overall. Deoxyribose is ribose with one less oxygen atom, hence the name.*

Sagittarius B2 contains the building blocks of the nucleic acids among its storehouse of chemical compounds. Molecules of the sugar glycoaldehyde ($HOCH_2$-CHO) are among the compounds found in the cloud, and these are known to react eagerly with other carbon compounds to form ribose. It is perhaps a slight exaggeration to say that we have found the building blocks of RNA and DNA in space, but we have certainly found the building blocks of the building blocks – and in a significant development announced in 2019, a team headed by Yasuhiro Oba announced that they had manufactured the components of DNA in a laboratory experiment designed to mimic the conditions that exist in interstellar clouds. As Jim Lovelock, originator of Gaia theory, has put it: 'It seems almost as if our Galaxy were a giant warehouse containing the spare parts needed for life.' But even if the spare parts needed for life exist in profusion in space, and in particular in rings of dust around stars like IRS 46, how could these building blocks have got down to Earth when our planet was young?

....

* I go into more detail about the structure of DNA and RNA in my discussion of Pillar Six.

The ice that covers grains of dust in space and provides a place where organic molecules can grow is also a key to how planets like the Earth can form. When a star forms by collapsing from a huge cloud of gas and dust as gravity tugs the material together, some dust gets left behind in a ring, like the one around IRS 46. Such a collapse is never perfectly symmetrical, because everything is rotating one way or another, so the dust settles down into a ring orbiting the parent star. If it were only dust, it would probably stay like that. But because they are covered in ice, the grains are tacky and tend to stick together when they collide, building up larger and larger lumps until they become big enough for their own gravity to pull other grains onto them. Then, the lumps can get together to make chunks of rock, colliding and merging, building bigger chunks and growing to become planets. The final stages of this process are extremely violent, with planetoids perhaps as big as Mars smashing into one another to make full-blown planets in the form of balls of molten rock. By that time, all the organics in the original grains that formed the planet – let's call it Earth – have been destroyed by the heat. But even after the Earth had formed there were still huge lumps of rocky material, many containing large amounts of ice of one kind or another, and dusty stuff around the young Sun.

The icy lumps became comets, and both comets and rocky lumps containing little or no ice were flung by Jupiter's gravity into elliptical orbits which took them through the inner part of the Solar System where the young Earth, sterile and lacking an atmosphere, was solidifying and cooling. The result was a huge number of impacts on the surface of the Earth, so extreme that astronomers refer to it as the Late Heavy Bombardment, or LHB. Among other things, the LHB was responsible for the battered appearance of the surface of the Moon, which was already orbiting the Earth at that time. Analysis of the pattern of lunar cratering and dating of Moon rocks reveals information about the LHB, which lasted for a few hundred million years, until most of the debris in the inner Solar System left over from the formation of the planets was used up. It ended a bit less than 4 billion years ago. In less than another 200 million years, protein- and nucleic acid-based life was established on Earth, thanks to a more gentle rain of material from space that continued to fall on our planet in the aftermath of the LHB.

Comets brought both water and life – or at least the precursors of life – down to Earth. Computer simulations of these events tell us that about ten times as much water as there is in the oceans today, and a thousand times as much gas as there is in the atmosphere today, would have been released during the cometary bombardment. This helped to cool the planet, while some of the volatile material, things like water, carbon dioxide and methane, escaped into space. But as the surface of the Earth was churned up by the impacts – a process graphically referred to as 'impact ploughing' – some of the material combined with the original material of the surface to form the rocks rich in volatiles which are typical of the Earth's crust today. Once there was an atmosphere and oceans, the Earth was ready for life. And it was immediately seeded with the ingredients of life.

As well as the comets that smashed violently into the young Earth, there were many more similar objects passing through the inner part of the Solar System and gradually being evaporated away by the heat of the Sun. This is the process which gives comets their characteristic tails today, although there were many more comets, with even more impressive tails, when the Earth and Solar System were young. After 4 billion years, most of the inner Solar System comets have long since boiled away. But that is why we are here. The tail of a comet is a stream of gas and dust escaping from the icy nucleus as the comet evaporates. That dust is left in a trail around the orbit of the comet, and even today the Earth often passes through such a stream of cometary dust, producing showers of meteors as tiny particles, about the size of grains of sand, burn up in the atmosphere. But there are also particles with a more open structure, like snowflakes, which settle down through the atmosphere of the Earth and reach the ground. They carry with them the same mixture of organic material that is seen (by spectroscopy) in comet tails, and which laces the giant clouds from which planetary systems form. Samples of this material have been collected using high-flying aircraft and stratospheric balloons. The amount collected shows that even today this process is delivering about 300 tonnes of organic matter – polyatomic molecules containing carbon – to the surface of the Earth each year.

As Darwin pointed out, there is no chance for this material to develop into life today. For a start, much of it is destroyed by reactions with oxygen in the atmosphere, and the rest will get into the food chain of living things. But there was no oxygen, and no living things, when the Earth had just cooled and gained an ocean and atmosphere. So how much of this cometary manna was there to kick-start the emergence of life?

Astronomers get a rough idea from things like studies of craters on the Moon, analyses of the orbits of comets today, and computer simulations of the dynamics of the young Solar System. According to their estimates, in a span of about 300,000 years starting from the end of the Late Heavy Bombardment, as much organic material fell to Earth as there is in everything alive on Earth today. In the time from the end of the LHB to when we know for sure there was life on Earth, about 200 million years, if all the organic matter that fell could have been preserved and spread out evenly over the surface of the planet, it would have made a layer containing 20 grams of organic stuff – up to and possibly including amino acids and ribose – on every square centimetre of the surface. This is equivalent to the contents of a 250g tub of butter on every 3.5 × 3.5 cm square of the Earth's surface. No wonder life got started so quickly – and once the first life got going, it would have had plenty of stuff to feed on in the early millennia.

This is now a pillar of science. The young Earth was seeded with the raw materials of life from the cosmic warehouse referred to by Lovelock. But there is a more speculative idea, which is today maybe somewhere between stages (i) and (ii) of Haldane's classification. There is no reason to doubt that amino acids and (probably) ribose exist in interstellar clouds. Could things have gone a stage further, to produce proteins and nucleic acids inside comets? The idea is not as crazy as you might think, because the trigger which collapses a cloud of gas and dust to form stars and planets is often a supernova, the explosion of a star. This produces radioactive elements, and in the cloud icy lumps of material laced with radioactive elements could get warm enough to melt water in their hearts through the heat generated by radioactive decay. Could Darwin's warm little ponds have existed in these lumps of ice even before the Earth formed? You can decide for yourself whether this speculation is (i) worthless nonsense; or (ii) an interesting, but perverse, point of view. But if true, it implies that at least in our immediate cosmic neighbourhood, life on other planets will be based on the same kind of proteins and nucleic acids that we are based on.

Even without going that far, however, we can be sure that any Earth-like planets out there will be seeded with similar precursors of life to those that we know exist in interstellar clouds. It is hard to see how life could fail to get started under those conditions – we don't know exactly how the step from non-living to living occurs, but the fact that it occurred so swiftly on Earth suggests that it is not difficult. This is powerful evidence that Giordano Bruno was right – there really may be a profusion of planets like our own, each one inhabited by life forms built up from the same material that we are made of.

Which raises another question. How did the atoms that make up organic molecules – things like carbon, nitrogen, oxygen and hydrogen – get into clouds of gas and dust in space? Those supernova explosions provide part of the answer. But before they could play their part, complex nuclear reactions had to take place inside stars, and those reactions hinge upon another of the pillars of science, a coincidence so astonishing that it almost beggars belief.

PILLAR

The Carbon Coincidence

A combination of spectroscopy and an understanding of the physics of stellar interiors tells us that a star like the Sun is composed almost entirely of hydrogen and helium, with just a smattering of heavier elements (Pillar Two). In the heart of a star, these elements are not in the form of gases, as they would be on Earth today. The electrons have been stripped from their nuclei, which are squeezed together at enormous densities, without the empty space that makes up ordinary atomic matter (Pillar One). Observations of clouds of gas in space tell us that they have a similar composition, although there the elements are in their familiar atomic state, with the dust that is so important to life as we know it a barely significant fraction of the total amount of stuff in a galaxy like our Milky Way. There may be other things that contribute to the overall mass of the Universe, things called Dark Matter and Dark Energy, but they are outside the scope of the present book. What matters here is the kind of stuff we are made of, the chemical elements we learned about in school, referred to by physicists as baryonic matter. Where does it come from?

There is a wealth of evidence that the Universe as we know it emerged from a very hot, very dense state, known as the Big Bang, about 13.8 billion years ago. The evidence comes partly from observations that the Universe is expanding today, so that it must have been more compact in the past, partly from studies of radio noise left over from the primordial fireball (the so-called Cosmic Microwave Background Radiation) and partly from our understanding of the laws of physics. Basic physics tells us that the first baryonic matter produced from the energy of the Big Bang, in line with Einstein's famous equation, would have been hydrogen, the simplest and lightest element. The equations also tell us that as the Universe expanded and cooled about 25 per cent of that hydrogen would have been converted into helium by nuclear fusion reactions while the young Universe was still hot. But after about three minutes the fireball in which the Universe was born would have cooled to the point where no more nuclear reactions could take place, leaving great clouds made of a mixture of hydrogen and helium, the raw material of the first stars and galaxies, moving apart from one another in the expanding Universe. It doesn't take a great intellectual leap to realise that the other elements must have been manufactured later on, inside stars. But how?

To put things in perspective, and see just how much (or how little!) stuff we are talking about, we can look at the composition of the Solar System, which is representative of what we might expect to find in planetary systems orbiting other stars. As we saw earlier, in terms of mass the Sun is 71 per cent hydrogen, 27 per cent helium, and less than 2 per cent of everything else put together. In terms of the number of atoms, hydrogen makes up 91.2 per cent of the Sun, helium 8.7 per cent, and everything else just 0.1 per cent. But when the Sun was young, a lot of the lighter stuff was blown away from the dusty disc in which planets formed by the heat of the young star. The planets, and ourselves, were made from what was left over. Taking the Solar System as a whole, because some of the light stuff has been lost, in terms of mass, hydrogen contributes 70.13 per cent, helium 27.87 per cent, and oxygen, the third most common element by mass, 0.91 per cent. Although hydrogen is important in the chemistry of life (remember CHON), there is no mystery about its origin, so we can put it to one side and look at the composition of the 2 per cent of the Solar System made of relatively heavy elements, where the quantities are so small that it makes sense to talk in terms of numbers of atoms rather than mass.

Taking just the top ten elements, but not attempting to give exact numbers for the quantities of hydrogen and helium (the top two), for every 70 atoms of oxygen there are 40 atoms of carbon, nine atoms of nitrogen, five atoms of silicon, four atoms each of magnesium and neon, three atoms of iron, and two atoms of sulphur. There are only five other elements (aluminium, argon, calcium, nickel-iron, and sodium) which have abundances between 10 per cent and 50 per cent of the abundance of sulphur. All the even heavier elements are very much rarer. For every 10 million atoms of sulphur there are, for example, only three atoms of gold, which is one of the reasons that gold is valuable, and which tells us something profound about the Universe which I shall come to shortly.

The first clue to how the elements are made inside stars comes from that list of the top ten – or at least, the members of the top ten heavier than helium. The nucleus of a helium atom (strictly speaking an atom of helium-4) is identical to an alpha particle, made up of two protons and two neutrons. A carbon nucleus is made up of six protons and six neutrons, like three alpha particles stuck together, which give it the name carbon-12. Adding another alpha particle gives you oxygen. Nitrogen, silicon, magnesium, neon and iron all have nuclei which contain whole numbers of alpha particles. If alpha particles can be added to nuclei inside stars, they will build up exactly this chain of elements. Rarer elements can be produced by occasional nuclear processes involving stray particles such as electrons, neutrons and protons interacting with the most common nuclei. This build-up of heavier elements can happen because the balance of energy involved favours heavier (more massive) nuclei over lighter ones, as with the conversion of hydrogen into helium, all the way up to iron. A nucleus of carbon-12, for example, is slightly less massive than three alpha particles, and if three alpha particles are combined (by whatever means) into one carbon-12 nucleus, the 'lost' mass is released as energy. Similarly, in terms of the overall energy, an oxygen nucleus is a more efficient arrangement than a carbon nucleus with a separate alpha particle, and so on up to iron. Even heavier elements are a separate puzzle, because their nuclei are less efficient packages of mass-energy, so it requires an input of energy to force nuclei to squeeze into one another to make elements such as gold. But first things first. In the 1940s, when the pioneering astrophysicist Fred Hoyle tackled the problem of what became known as stellar nucleosynthesis, he started with the puzzle of making everything up to iron inside stars.

Nuclear fusion releases energy when lighter nuclei join together to make heavier nuclei, up to iron. But all nuclei have a positive electric charge, and are repelled from one another by electrical forces. They can only fuse if they are squeezed so tightly together that nuclear forces overwhelm the electric force which tries to keep the nuclei apart. This means they have to be moving very fast when they collide, and their speed is related to the temperature. By the mid-1940s, physicists had a good idea of the temperatures required to do this for different fusion reactions, but there was a big problem with one of the first steps in the process of building up nuclei by adding alpha particles.

You may have noticed I haven't mentioned any nucleus composed of two alpha particles. The element this corresponds to is called beryllium-8, but it is never found in nature. Beryllium-8 nuclei are unstable, and if they are manufactured

Fred Hoyle
A. Barrington Brown © Gonville & Caius College/Science Photo Library

artificially they fall apart almost instantly. A couple of astrophysicists suggested that the way to get across the gap between helium-4 and carbon-12 would be if three alpha particles came together simultaneously inside a star, fusing to make a single nucleus of carbon-12 without beryllium-8 having been formed along the way. But such a triple collision would involve so much kinetic energy that it would be more like a train wreck than a smooth fusing of alpha particles. How could such a process proceed smoothly?

Hoyle's insight started with the realisation that there is no need for the three alpha particles to collide literally simultaneously. Although the lifetime of beryllium-8 is small – each nucleus lasts for only about 10^{-19} seconds – under the conditions that exist at the heart of a star there are so many alpha particles that collisions are constantly manufacturing them. There are always some around, just as there is always some water in a sink being fed by an open tap while water is escaping from the plughole. In a star with a central temperature of around 100 million degrees C, about one nucleus in every 10 billion will be beryllium-8. So there is always a population of beryllium nuclei which are 'targets' for alpha particles, opportunities to make carbon-12 nuclei. But even this prospect didn't look promising, because it couldn't make enough carbon to explain the amount seen in the Universe unless another factor was at work.

In 1953, Hoyle realised what the other factor was. All nuclei can exist in different energy states, called resonances.

The usual analogy is with a plucked guitar string. This has a fundamental note, but it can also play different harmonics of that note. Nuclei have a basic energy level (the ground state), but if they are given extra energy they can jump up to an 'excited' state, like a ball being lifted up a staircase to a higher step. Like the ball bouncing down the stairs, such excited nuclei will soon give up the extra energy (perhaps in the form of gamma rays) and settle back into the ground state.

Hoyle calculated that under the conditions inside a star, other things being equal the collision of an alpha particle with a short-lived beryllium nucleus would simply blow it apart. But he reasoned that if the energy of the incoming particle was just right, it would nudge the combined nucleus gently into an excited state of carbon-12, like a ball being gently placed on a high step of a staircase, from which it could radiate energy and jump down into the ground state of carbon-12. The snag was, the trick only worked if there was an excited state of the carbon-12 nucleus at a very precise energy level, 7.65 million electron Volts above the ground state, in the units used by physicists. If the energy level was even 5 per cent higher the trick would not work. And nobody knew if there was such an excited state of carbon-12 at all.

Nobody took Hoyle's idea seriously. But his argument seemed to him to be watertight. Carbon exists in the Universe. Indeed, we are made partly of carbon. It has to have been made somewhere – and where else could it have been made other than inside stars? At the time Hoyle, although based in the UK at Cambridge, was visiting the California Institute of Technology, and took the opportunity to ask an experimental physicist, William Fowler, to carry out an experiment to test his idea, looking for the predicted resonance of carbon-12. Actually, he did more than request. He badgered Fowler into submission. Fowler told me that he thought Hoyle was crazy, but he eventually agreed to put a small team together to do the experiment to shut him up. Whatever the motivation, the experiment got done. It took three months, and it proved Hoyle was right. There is indeed a carbon resonance in just the right place to explain how the 'triple alpha' process works. Everybody was surprised – everybody except Hoyle.

This is one of the greatest triumphs of science, perhaps the single most significant example of a theory making a prediction and being proved right by a laboratory experiment. It was well worthy of a Nobel Prize, but Hoyle never received one, although Fowler did, for the work which both of them and two other colleagues developed from this beginning.

On his next visit to Caltech, Hoyle got to know the British husband-and-wife team Geoffrey and Margaret Burbidge, who were temporarily based in California (they eventually moved there permanently) and were trying to understand the significance of the exact abundances of various elements in stars, as revealed by spectroscopy. Fowler got roped in to this work as well, with the team calculating how a steady supply of neutrons inside stars could convert nuclei produced by the alpha process into other elements in the proportions actually observed. Hoyle initially kept in touch with the work from a distance, but in 1956 all four were together in California, where they put everything in place in a massive scientific paper that was published in the October 1957 issue of the *Reviews of Modern Physics*. The names of the authors of this masterwork are listed alphabetically, as Burbidge, Burbidge, Fowler and Hoyle, and to this day it is referred to simply as B^2FH.* But everybody knew that the guiding inspiration for the work came from Hoyle – everybody except the Nobel Foundation, which eventually, in 1983, gave Fowler alone the prize for this breakthrough. Fowler was embarrassed, but accepted the award. When Fowler died, Geoffrey Burbidge referred to the decision in his obituary of his old friend, saying that this award 'caused some strain among B^2FH, since we were all aware that it was a team effort and the original work was done by Fred Hoyle'. But the work stands as a pillar of science, whoever got the recognition. Without this coincidence between the carbon resonance and the amount of energy carried by a fast-moving alpha particle inside a star, there would be no carbon, no heavier elements, no complex molecules in the gas clouds from which stars form, no planets like Earth, and no life forms like us in the Universe.

This work essentially explained how all of the elements are manufactured inside stars, up to iron-56 and nickel-56 (iron-56 contains 26 protons and 30 neutrons in each nucleus;

* Pronounced 'B-squared F H'.

nickel-56 has 28 protons and 28 neutrons in each nucleus, fourteen alpha particles fused together). The manufacture of even heavier elements involves some of the most violent events seen in the Universe today, when whole stars explode as supernovae. Fowler and Hoyle (speaking alphabetically) were also involved in developing this understanding of stellar nucleosynthesis. But that understanding has since been extended to take on board studies of even more violent events.

The supernova connection involves stars much more massive than our Sun. For stars with masses about one to four times the mass of our Sun, after the conversion of hydrogen to helium in its core the star shrinks a little, gets hotter in the middle, and 'burns' helium into a mixture of carbon and oxygen. But that is as far as it goes. During the later stages of its life, the star blows a lot of material, including carbon and oxygen, out into space, then settles down as a white dwarf – a cooling cinder with a mass close to that of the Sun today, but no bigger than the Earth. More massive stars lead more interesting, and spectacular, lives. The extra mass is important because more inward pressure is required to get the interior of the star hot enough for successive phases of nuclear burning to take place. Carbon is converted into neon, sodium and magnesium, by the processes studied by B^2FH, at a temperature of about 400 million degrees C; oxygen burning produces silicon, sulphur and other elements at a temperature of about 1,000 million degrees C. The silicon-28 (effectively seven alpha particles stuck together) produced in this way is eventually converted into iron and nickel. But at each stage of the process, a residue is left behind, so that a massive star at the end of its life contains a core of hydrogen, surrounded by a shell of helium, surrounded by successive shells of other elements nested like onion skins.

When all its sources of nuclear energy are exhausted, the star will collapse. But this releases gravitational energy, generating so much heat that the star explodes as a supernova. Some of the explosion goes inward, compressing the core of the star and turning it into a neutron star (with as much mass as our Sun squeezed into a ball about 20 km across), or even a black hole. But a great deal of the blast goes outwards. It provides the energy which manufactures elements heavier than iron in the outer part of the star, and also spreads these elements, and the others built up during the life of the star, out across space to form the raw material for new stars and planets – and, on at least one of those planets, people.

All this was clear by the end of the 1960s, although many details were filled in over the decades that followed. But there was a nagging problem. Even though the traces of very heavy elements such as gold seen in the Universe are small, the ever-improving calculations and computer simulations showed that a supernova explosion could not make enough of them to explain the observations. Matching up the observed rate of supernova explosions with the observed amount of things like gold, platinum and uranium in the Universe, scientists found that only half of the very heavy elements could be accounted for in this way. Something else was required to make the rest, and without knowing exactly what it might be, astronomers gave it a name – a kilonova. Completing the story of the origin of the elements, and confirming the accuracy of those calculations dating all the way back to Hoyle's insight, kilonova explosions were detected at last in 2017, but not (initially) by their light.

On 14 September 2015, astronomers opened a new window on the Universe. For the first time, they detected gravitational waves – ripples in space – from a violent event far away across the Universe. That event was the merger of two black holes. The discovery of gravitational waves had long been anticipated – they are a prediction of Einstein's general theory of relativity – and long sought. But they are incredibly tiny, by the time they reach Earth, and very hard to observe. The 'telescopes' that made the observation were based around evacuated tubes 4 km long, in which mirrors that reflected laser light to and fro along the tunnels were so delicately balanced and so precisely monitored that when the mirrors moved across a distance less than the diameter of an atom, the wobble could be measured.* Einstein's theory predicts exactly what kind of wobble would be produced by waves from things like merging black holes, and that kind of wobble was precisely what was detected in September 2015. Since then, the detectors around

....

* For details, see https://www.amazon.co.uk/Discovering-Gravitational -Waves-Kindle-Single-ebook/dp/B071FFJT74

the world (there are now two in the United States and one each in Europe and India) have found several other gravitational wave 'events', as the astronomers like to call them, and one in particular is relevant to my story.

On 17 August 2017 the detectors picked up a slightly different pattern of ripples, lasting for just 100 seconds, which matched the predictions of the pattern that would be produced when two neutron stars collided with one another. This was especially exciting because unlike the merger of two black holes, a neutron star collision was expected to produce an explosion of light and other radiation, such as gamma rays. Neutron star mergers were, indeed, probable candidates for the hypothetical kilonova explosions in which very heavy elements might be formed, and astronomers had calculated, based on the number of stars around in a galaxy like our own, how common such events might be.* The direction the gravitational waves had come from was indicated approximately by the observations, and within hours of the detection astronomers were pointing their telescopes in that direction. They found a short-lived bright object in a nearby galaxy called NGC 4993, roughly 130 million light years away from us. It was a kilonova. Spectroscopy showed that the kilonova had indeed produced a lot of heavy elements, such as uranium,

---

* Because neutron stars are so dense, these collisions are very efficient at making heavy elements, but they only produce about a tenth as much light as a supernova, so they are harder to find.

gold and platinum. This included 200 times the mass of the Earth in the form of gold, and 500 Earth-masses of platinum. When the amount seen in this explosion was multiplied by the calculated frequency of neutron star mergers, the result was that such explosions could indeed produce the 'missing' half of the heavies. Among other things, this means that if you have a wedding ring or some other item made of gold or platinum, you can be sure that very many of the atoms in this object were manufactured during the collision of two neutron stars, and spread into space in a gigantic explosion, seeding the cloud from which the Sun and Earth formed.

So we know how the elements are made in stars, we know that those elements are combined into complex organic molecules in space, and we know that these complex molecules were brought gently down to the surface of the Earth soon after it formed, where they became the key components of life. But how do those components work together to make things like us? The answer involves another surprising pillar of science.

PILLAR

The Book of Life is Written in Three-letter Words

The complexity of life is built from two families of molecules – proteins and nucleic acids. These molecules are themselves built from a relatively modest variety of compounds. There are 92 elements that occur naturally on Earth, but just 27 of them are essential for living things, and not all of the 27 are found in all living things.

Proteins have two roles to play. One kind provides the structure of the body – things like hair, muscle, feathers, fingernails and shells. A combination of X-ray analysis, chemistry, and an understanding of the quantum mechanical processes that hold atoms together to make molecules has shown that these proteins are made from long chains of amino acids, forming a helical structure. It's fairly obvious that this kind of molecule can produce long, thin things like hair, but it can also produce hard sheets of stuff like fingernails when the individual helices are linked together side by side by chemical bonds of one kind or another. All of this was established by

Linus Pauling and his colleagues at the California Institute of Technology, who published a groundbreaking series of seven papers on the structure of proteins in the journal *Proceedings of the National Academy of Sciences* in 1951. The other kind of protein provides the workers of the body. Things like the haemoglobin that carries oxygen around in your blood, and substances known as enzymes that encourage (or in some cases inhibit) certain chemical reactions that are important to life. Unravelling their structure proved a tougher nut to crack.

A clue to why this kind of protein is hard to deconstruct comes from the name they were eventually given – globular proteins. It turned out that they are also made of long chains of amino acids, but that in this case the chains are curled up into little balls, and each kind of globular protein has its own distinctive three-dimensional shape. It is the shape of a globular protein, as much as its chemical composition, which determines its role in the chemical processes of life. For example, haemoglobin has a cavity which is just the right size and shape for a molecule of oxygen to nestle in. Or think of a globular protein which has two indentations, each just right for a different smaller molecule to sit in. When they do so, they will be aligned in such a way that bonds can form between them, before they are released as a single larger molecule. This is reminiscent of the way small molecules got together on the surfaces of icy grains in the depths of space before the Earth formed. One enzyme may, for example, mindlessly and repeatedly join together specific pairs of amino acids to make one link in a growing chain that will become another protein molecule.

The structure of haemoglobin itself was worked out by 1959, by researchers funded by the UK Medical Research Council laboratory. It is made up of four chains, each made of similar amino acids, locked together to make a roughly spherical ball which actually has four pockets on its surface where oxygen molecules can nestle. And almost identical chains are found doing exactly the same job in the blood of creatures as different as horses and whales. Evolution is very conservative – once it has found a molecule that is good at doing a specific job, it sticks with that molecule without replacing it. But how does it know how to make these molecules? This is where nucleic acids come in to the story, although it took a long time for the role of DNA and RNA to be appreciated.

When the nucleic acids were first identified as major components of living cells, it was thought that they were some kind of structural material, like scaffolding, to which the much more complex and (it was thought) more interesting protein molecules were attached. It was a simple mistake to make, because on the face of things DNA and RNA molecules are themselves simple. Each of them is a long molecule made up of four sub-units called bases. Three of these are the same in both RNA and DNA; the fourth base is different in the two molecules, so there are five bases involved in all. They are uracil (U), thymine (T), cytosine (C), adenine (A) and guanine (G). DNA molecules contain G, A, C, and T, while RNA molecules contain G, A, C, and U. U, T, and C are built around six-sided rings of carbon and nitrogen atoms, while A and G are based on two such rings joined side by side, like a figure 8. These bases are attached to a backbone containing the relevant sugars (ribose or deoxyribose) linked together in a chain, with the bases sticking out to the side of the backbone. The details of this were not known, however, until the early 1950s, when Francis Crick and James Watson in Cambridge used X-ray data obtained by Rosalind Franklin and Raymond Gosling at King's College in London, which had been passed to Watson by a colleague without their knowledge or permission, to determine the famous 'double helix' structure of DNA. The original idea was that the bases were laid out in a regular way along pieces of scaffolding – something like GACTGACTGACTGACT … in DNA and GACUGACUGACUGACU … in RNA. This is not a 'message' that conveys much information.

That was more or less where things stood in the mid-1940s. It was known that the genetic material that passes on the blueprint, or recipe, for life is contained in large structures called chromosomes found in the hearts of cells, and that these chromosomes are copied and passed on to later generations to carry the recipe forward. But chromosomes were known to contain both DNA and proteins, and the proteins were thought to be the important component for conveying information. One way in which a cell might 'know' how to make the proteins it needed to function might be, for example, if one sample of each protein was attached to the scaffolding of DNA, ready to

Raymond Gosling
King's College London Archives/Science Photo Library

be copied when required. It made sense, but it was wrong.*
Even so, it was clear that chromosomes carry the recipe of life,
in some form of 'code'.

The person who set scientists on the trail of that code of life
was a physicist, Erwin Schrödinger, best known today as the
originator of the famous 'cat paradox' of quantum mechanics.†
In 1943, Schrödinger was based at the Institute for Advanced
Studies in Dublin, where he had moved as a refugee from the
Nazis after their takeover of Austria. That year, he gave a series
of lectures at Trinity College on the theme 'What is Life?' They
were published the following year in a book with the same
title. This book would have a huge influence on the generation
of scientists who set out to crack the code of life after the end
of the Second World War, including Crick and Watson.

The key idea that Schrödinger introduced and passed on
to those researchers was that 'the most essential part of a living cell – the chromosome fibre – may suitably be called *an
aperiodic crystal*'.‡ He thought that the key component of a
chromosome was protein, but that doesn't matter, because his
insight works equally well for fibres made of DNA. A periodic
crystal, to use his terminology, would be something like the
structure of common salt, sodium chloride, in which alternating atoms of sodium (Na) and chlorine (Cl) form a repetitive

....

* Almost the opposite of the truth; in chromosomes, proteins are the
structural material and DNA carries the information, as I shall explain.
† See my book *Six Impossible Things*.
‡ His emphasis.

array in three dimensions, NaClNaClNaClNaCl ... which has a structure but conveys very little information. This is very similar to the idea of DNA as the scaffolding on which proteins might be hung. What Schrödinger meant by an aperiodic crystal can be understood in terms of a tapestry. If you had some strands of a few colours of thread, they might be arranged side by side and woven to make bands of colour – for example, red, yellow, blue and green – in a striped blanket. This would be equivalent to a periodic crystal. Or the same threads could be woven in a more complicated way to make a picture of a flower. This would be equivalent to an aperiodic crystal. Schrödinger pointed out that although it is made up in this way from strands with just a few different colours, there is a structure in 'a Raphael tapestry which shows no dull repetition but an elaborate, coherent, meaningful design'.

Schrödinger also pointed out that what he referred to as a 'code-script' carried by an aperiodic crystal in the chromosome fibres could contain all the information required to make proteins, without it being necessary for a copy of each kind of protein to be carried as a template in the chromosomes themselves. Just 20 different amino acids are required to make all of the different proteins important for life, and if you think of these amino acids as 'words' strung out along a protein molecule to make a sentence (or a book!) you would have nearly as much scope for conveying information as the 26 letters in the English alphabet which I am using to write this book, which (I hope you agree) contains a lot more information than a boring repetition of the alphabet from A to Z. But would you need even a 20-letter alphabet to write the book of life?

There is no need, Schrödinger realised, for anything as complicated as amino acids. Even individual atoms could do the job if they could be organised properly: 'The number of [different] atoms in such a structure [the aperiodic crystal] need not be very large to produce an almost unlimited number of possible arrangements.' He gave as an example the Morse code, where there are just two basic signs, dot and dash, but which can be put together in groups of up to four symbols to make 30 different specifications, sufficient for the English alphabet plus a few punctuation marks. And with a third sign, using them in groups of not more than ten symbols, 'you could form 88,572 different "letters"; with five signs and groups up to 25, the number is 372,529,029,846,191,405'. Schrödinger got a bit carried away by his training as a physicist here, since there is no need for such a fantastically high number of words. But that really only became clear after the structure of DNA had been determined.

That story is too well-known for it to be necessary to go into detail here, but what matters is that each molecule of DNA is composed of two strands, twining around each other in the famous double helix. Each single strand of DNA has a spine made of a chain of sugar groups linked together by phosphate groups (a phosphate group is made of a phosphate atom surrounded by four oxygen atoms). As we saw earlier, the bases

(G, A, T, and C) are attached to the sugar groups, and stick out from the sides of the spine. Different pairs of these bases have an affinity for one another, thanks to their shape and to a weak form of electric attraction called the hydrogen bond. Thymine and adenine naturally link together in this way, as do cytosine and guanine. This holds the two strands of DNA together, but relatively loosely. Everywhere on one strand that there is T, on the opposite strand there is A; everywhere on one strand there is C, on the opposite strand there is G. And vice versa. This pairing was the key to the Crick–Watson model of DNA, and at the end of their famous paper, published in *Nature* in 1953, they rather coyly stated:

> It has not escaped our notice that the specific pairing we have postulated immediately suggests a possible copying mechanism for the genetic material.

Which was their ploy to establish their priority* for the idea that DNA can be replicated if the two strands untwist and then each strand builds a new partner for itself by hooking up with other components from the chemical soup inside the cell. Every A on a single strand captures a T from the soup, every T captures an A, every G captures a C, and every C captures a G. The result is two identical double helices where there used to be one. Genetic material has been copied. Exactly how

....

* The ploy worked, as the fact that I am quoting it here proves.

the mechanisms of the cell do this was far from being understood in 1953, but the important point was that clearly this was something that could work, in principle. The big question this raised was, what was it that was being copied? How did DNA store the information in the book of life?

It was another physicist, the Russian-born American George Gamow, who set people, in particular Francis Crick, on the trail. He later recalled that in 1953, while a visitor at the Berkeley campus of the University of California:

> I was walking through the corridor in Radiation Lab, and there was Luis Alvarez going with *Nature* in his hand … he said 'Look, what a wonderful article Watson and Crick have written.' This was the first time that I saw it. And then I returned to Washington and started thinking about it.*

Gamow came up with the idea that protein molecules could be built up directly along strands of DNA, if the row of bases along the DNA carried the code for each amino acid required for the protein in the right order along the DNA molecule. This echoed Schrödinger's idea, which he was unaware of. Gamow wrote to Watson and Crick with his idea, and spelled it out in a paper in *Nature* published in 1954:

---

* Interview in the George Gamow Collection of the Library of Congress, Washington, DC.

The hereditary properties of any given organism could be characterised by a long number written in a four-digital system. On the other hand, the [proteins] are long peptide chains formed by about twenty different kinds of amino acids … the question arises about the way in which four-digit numbers can be translated into [amino acids].

The details of Gamow's idea were wrong, but by talking about the code of life in this way he prompted Crick and many others to try to work out how such 'translation' might work. A key step was understanding the role of the other nucleic acid, RNA.

One puzzle about how DNA could be actively involved in the workings of a cell is that the DNA is packed away at the heart of the cell, in its nucleus. All the action, including manufacturing protein, takes place in the outer part of the cell, the cytoplasm. There is very little DNA out there but plenty of RNA. And although the amount of DNA in every cell of a particular organism is the same for every cell and all the time, the amount of RNA varies considerably from cell to cell and from time to time in any individual cell. It became clear that it is RNA that is directly involved in making protein, and that bits of genetic code are copied from the DNA onto new strands of RNA as required, then the RNA is released out into the cytoplasm and used to build up protein molecules roughly in the way Gamow suggested, after which the RNA strands are broken up and the parts reused. DNA is like a library, a storehouse of information, from which individual books, instruction manuals for the manufacture of specific proteins, are copied onto RNA as required. When part of a DNA molecule in the nucleus is uncoiled and copied onto RNA using the mechanism which had 'not escaped the notice' of Crick and Watson, each T is replaced by a U, but there is no other significant difference. So for simplicity, when discussing the genetic code from now on I shall describe it in terms of the RNA bases, U, C, G, and A.

Cracking the code involved a lot of people carrying out a lot of biochemical investigations, unravelling the details of the workings of the cell step by step. But this is not the place to go into all those details, which you can find in Horace Judson's book,* and I shall focus on the thinking behind the experiments, and the conclusions resulting from the experiments. Very early on, the researchers decided to concentrate on a triplet code, not the four-digital code suggested by Gamow, because three letters are all you need. If you have four bases and treat each of them as a letter, then using each one individually you can only code for four amino acids. With two bases at a time in doublets, you can manage sixteen different arrangements – sixteen words, not enough to code for the 20 amino acids essential for life. But with three-letter words, or triplets, you can manage 64 different combinations, more than enough to code for all the necessary amino acids, with

....
* See Further Reading.

some left over to act as the equivalent of punctuation marks, including markers for the beginning and end of a particular 'message'. With a four-letter code, the number of individual words would be 256, far more than required.

During the 1950s and 1960s, biochemists carried out experiments involving strands of RNA made up of a variety of bases, to see what kind of proteins they manufactured. A key breakthrough came with the discovery that a boring strand of RNA carrying the repeating chain of bases UUUUU ... (poly-U), when placed in a suitable chemical environment mimicking the inside of a cell, would make a boring chain made of repeating units of the amino acid phenylalanine, phe. phe.phe ... (poly-phe). This is technically a protein, but of no use to living things. It meant, however, that the first triplet word had been identified. The code UUU in RNA corresponds to the amino acid phe. A huge amount of work along these lines led to a complete understanding of the code. Every one of the triplets that can be formed out of the bases U, C, G, and A was linked with a specific amino acid or with a punctuation mark. Some of the amino acids are coded for by several triplets – for example, valine can be indicated by GUU, GUC, GUA or GUG – but this redundancy does not affect the way the book of life is read. Surprising though it may seem, the whole story of life really is written in three-letter words. But you need a lot of words to tell that story.

How big is the book? In human cells, the DNA packaged into chromosomes in the nucleus is coiled up in coils which are themselves coiled into supercoils. There are roughly 3 billion pairs of bases, linked across DNA strands, in each of the cells, packed so tightly that they take up a space only about six microns (six millionths of a metre) across. If all this DNA could be untwisted and stretched out, it would be about two metres long. And if all the DNA in all the cells in your body were stretched out in this way and laid end to end, it would stretch along about 16 billion kilometres – more than a thousand times the distance of the Earth from the Sun.

Exactly how bits of DNA are untwisted from this compact state and copied onto RNA when required is still not fully understood. But there is one key feature of the process which you may have already latched on to. It is only possible because the twin strands of a DNA molecule are only held together loosely, by the hydrogen bonds that I mentioned so casually earlier, so that they can be opened up and closed again like the opposite sides of a zip. Hydrogen bonding is a key to the existence of life as we know it, and it can be understood more easily in the context of another scientific surprise – the incredible lightness of ice.

PILLAR

The Incredible Lightness of Ice

Ice floats on water. This is so obvious that most of us never think about it. But it is a key feature of our environment, and it is distinctly odd, as a little home experiment indicates. If you take two see-through containers, and partly fill one with water and the other with olive oil, then put them into a freezer, the liquids will both solidify. The water makes ice, while the olive oil turns into a solid similar to butter. Now take the containers out and stand them on a warm table while they thaw. In one container, liquid water forms at the bottom as the ice melts, until all that is left is a layer of ice floating on top of the water. In the other, the lump at the bottom of the container stays solid, while molten oil rises to the surface, forming a liquid layer above the solid lump. The second situation is more representative of how things behave. Most solids are heavier (denser) than their liquid form so they sink. Why should ice be different, and how has that affected the evolution of life on Earth?

Although people had previously noticed what was sometimes called 'the expansion by cold' of water near its freezing point, the first person to carry out a proper scientific study of the phenomenon was Benjamin Thompson, Count Rumford, in the first decade of the nineteenth century. Rumford was a colourful character worthy of a book in his own right, who started life as plain Ben Thompson in the American colonies in 1753, fought on the British side in the American War of Independence, made his way after the war to Bavaria (where his many services to the Duke led to him being awarded the title of Count), made pioneering studies of the nature of heat, and founded the Royal Institution in London. Along the way, he investigated what happens to water as it approaches its freezing point.

It is typical of Rumford, who never switched off from work, that some of those investigations were triggered by observations he made while on holiday in the Swiss Alps with the beautiful Madame Marie Lavoisier (the widow of the pioneering chemist Antoine Lavoisier), whom he later married. On the surface of the great mass of ice on the Chamonix glacier, Rumford saw 'a pit perfectly cylindrical, about seven inches in diameter, and more than four feet deep, quite full of water'. After the guides told him that such pits are quite common, he reasoned out how they formed. Warm summer winds blowing over the ice could melt surface ice in gentle natural depressions. The water at the top of these puddles is a tiny bit warmer than the water lower down, so it is denser, sinks, and gives up its heat to the ice at the bottom of the puddle and melts it. The now slightly cooler water is lighter and rises to the

Count Rumford
Collection Abecasis/Science Photo Library

surface, being replaced by slightly warmer water falling down, in a perfect example of inverted convection, 'by which the depth of the pit is continually increased' until the cold weather returns. Rumford wrote all this up in a paper published in the *Philosophical Transactions* of the Royal Society in 1804, where he stressed that these studies:

> ought not to be regarded as suitable for determining with great exactness the temperature at which the density of water is at a maximum, but rather as proving that this temperature is really several degrees of the thermometric scale above that of melting ice.

But just a year later he presented a paper to the National Institute of France describing a neat experiment which did establish reasonably accurately the exact temperature at which water has its maximum density.

Rumford filled a container with ice on the point of melting, exactly at the freezing point of water. Inside the ice bath there was a second container, and inside that was a little cup-shaped receptacle, in contact with a thermometer. Directly above the cup there was a heated ball which could be dipped into the slush at the top of the ice bath, and warmed the water there. As Rumford anticipated, the warm water was denser than the icy water and flowed down into the cup; the densest water filled the cup, where its temperature could be measured. He found that the cup filled with water at 41 degrees Fahrenheit, equivalent to about 5 degrees Celsius (modern measurements give the temperature at which water has its maximum density as 4°C, so he did remarkably well with the equipment he had available).

The question this raised was, why did water behave in this way? The answer lies in the nature of the hydrogen bond, which was only properly understood after the development of quantum theory in the 1920s, but which you can get a rough idea of in general terms. It depends on the fact that the hydrogen atom is the simplest of all the elements, and has just a single negatively charged electron in some sense orbiting around a single positively charged proton.* Atoms can combine to form molecules when they share electrons with each other to form a link, and some configurations are particularly favoured by the quantum rules. For example, a hydrogen atom would 'like' to have two electrons, so it will eagerly join together with any other atom that has an electron available for pairing to make a molecule, with the two electrons shared between them. This is only possible for certain partners, because of the way the quantum rules affect the pairing. Carbon atoms, for example, can form four bonds, oxygen atoms two, and nitrogen three. But when hydrogen does form a bond in this way, with the electrons in a sense forming a bridge between a proton and another atom, the

....

* Only in some sense because quantum physics tells us that electrons do not behave purely as tiny particles, but have wave-like properties as well.

other side of each proton is exposed, with no screening of negative electric charge outside it. This means that it can form weaker links with atoms that have a surplus of negative charge, apart from the electrons used in ordinary bonding, available for this weaker form of pairing. This only happens for hydrogen atoms; nuclei of other atoms are screened by additional electrons not included in regular chemical bonding. But it is that very surplus of electrons that provides an opportunity for them to form the other end of hydrogen bonds.

Although hydrogen bonds can form between other molecules (not least in DNA, and in the links that give protein molecules their interesting and important shapes), the ones involving water are particularly strong and particularly important for us. Water molecules are made up of two hydrogen atoms and one oxygen atom, H_2O. Each oxygen nucleus contains eight protons, so there are eight electrons in the cloud surrounding the nucleus. Just two of these are involved in the bonds with the hydrogen atoms, so there are six unattached electrons in the cloud. These provide an electrical attraction for the partially exposed hydrogen nuclei belonging to nearby water molecules.*

Each oxygen atom in a water molecule can form two hydrogen bonds in this way, while on the other side of the water molecule each hydrogen atom can form a single hydrogen

....

* They cannot form 'proper' bonds for quantum-mechanical reasons beyond the scope of this book.

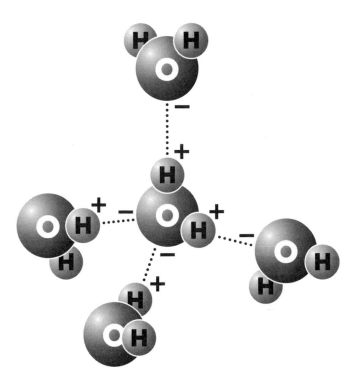

Hydrogen bonding of water molecules

bond with an oxygen atom in another molecule. This makes four bonding possibilities in all, encouraging the formation of hydrogen bonds arranged in a tetrahedron around each water molecule, which produces the open crystalline structure in the solid (think snowflakes), and also encourages water molecules to tug on one another as they move about in a liquid. Which is why water is liquid at all the temperatures we find comfortable on Earth today.

Whether a substance is in the form of a solid, liquid or gas depends on the temperature, other things (in particular pressure) being equal. The higher the temperature, the more energy the particles making up the substance (the atoms or molecules) have, so the faster they move. At high enough temperatures, they fly around freely, bouncing off each other and the walls of any container they are confined in. At a range of lower temperatures, they are almost touching, but still have enough energy to slide past one another. At still lower temperatures, they are scarcely able to move at all, except to do a kind of jogging on the spot, and form a solid. Heavier molecules need more energy to make them move faster, so by and large substances made of heavier molecules ought to melt and evaporate at higher temperatures than substances made of lighter molecules, except where the atoms link together to form crystals or other arrays, as with, for example, solid carbon. The peculiarity of water can be seen by comparing its behaviour with that of substances made up of molecules with roughly the same, or even greater, weight than molecules of water.

On a scale where a single hydrogen atom has one unit of mass, oxygen has 16 units, so a single oxygen molecule (H_2O) weighs in at 18 units. Another very common molecule, carbon dioxide, is made up of two oxygen molecules joined to a single atom of carbon, which has a mass of 12. So it has an overall mass of 44 units. Yet carbon dioxide is a gas at room temperature, while water is a liquid. Hydrogen sulphide (mass 34), methane (mass 16) and nitrogen dioxide (mass 46), among others, are all gases at room temperature. Water is only liquid under the conditions that exist at the surface of the Earth because hydrogen bonds make water molecules sticky. Even when the molecules are moving about in the form of a gas and the attraction between oxygen molecules is not strong enough to slow them down and form permanent hydrogen bonds, the hydrogen bonding effect still has an influence. In liquid water, although the distances between neighbouring molecules is large enough and the energy of the molecules is great enough that hydrogen bonds that try to form are stretched and broken, they still form temporarily. In a gas, the effect gets stronger when the temperature gets down towards the boiling point, 100°C; in liquid water itself, the molecules are closer together than they would be without the hydrogen bonding effect. And when the temperature gets close to freezing, the effect is dramatic.

Down to about 4°C things proceed roughly as you might expect, with the density increasing as the water cools and molecules move more slowly. Water at 4°C is about 4 per cent more dense than water near the boiling point. But below 4°C, the molecules are moving so slowly that they begin to arrange themselves in the tetrahedral pattern typical of ice. Even before they can form permanent crystals, this reduces the density of the liquid, just as Rumford observed. And when the solid ice does form, it floats on water. There are other substances that form spacious crystal lattices and expand on freezing, including acetic acid, silicon, gallium, and (if you want to risk it) plutonium. But water is of key importance to life on Earth, and the incredible lightness of ice may be a major reason why we are here.

There are several benefits of hydrogen bonding that may not be immediately obvious. For example, it allows animals such as us to cool down by sweating because a large amount of heat is needed to break hydrogen bonds between water molecules and make the water evaporate (it is the energy used in evaporating sweat that helps to cool us down on a hot day); and the proximity of a large body of water that can absorb heat when temperatures are high and let it out when temperatures are low reduces the range of temperature variations near the sea, keeping summers relatively cool and winters relatively warm. This is more than just a convenience for coastal dwellers today. It is the hydrogen bonding effect which allows the existence of large bodies of water even when the temperature drops below freezing, because a layer of ice on top of the water acts as an insulating blanket which keeps the water underneath the ice liquid. Without this effect, our planet might be a frozen, lifeless iceball, judging from the geological record.

If the hydrogen bond did not exist, there would, of course, be no liquid water on Earth at all. But imagine for a moment a planet cool enough for liquid water to exist without the benefit of hydrogen bonding. What would happen if it got cold enough for ice to form? The ice, being denser than liquid water, would settle to the bottom of the ocean. That would leave the top of the ocean exposed to the cold, so more water would freeze and sink to the bottom. Soon, the entire ocean, or lake, would be frozen solid. This would happen to all the water on the planet. It would be very difficult to thaw such a frozen planet, because the shiny white surface of the ice would reflect away the incoming solar heat. Life like us could not exist in such circumstances. And even with the benefit of hydrogen bonding, the Earth has been through more than one 'snowball' event during its long history.

Geological evidence in the form of scars in the rocks and the kinds of sediments deposited in the oceans at different times tells us that the Earth froze over entirely about 2.5 billion years ago, and froze again some time between 700 and 600 million years ago. There may have been other similar events, but the evidence for them is not conclusive. Nobody knows what causes such events. Speculations include vast volcanic outbursts on Earth which throw material high into the atmosphere and shield the surface from the Sun's heat, or collisions between asteroids in space that spread dust through

119

the inner part of the Solar System to make a sunscreen. But the important point is that once such a big freeze occurs, because of the reflectivity of the shiny surface of the planet it would be hard to have a big thaw. In fact, shiny ice is not really a good image of the appearance of snowball Earth. It would be so cold that tiny crystals of ice would form in the dry atmosphere and fall to the ground, where they would glitter like diamond dust.

The end of such a situation is almost certainly caused by a build-up of carbon dioxide in the air, warming the planet through the greenhouse effect. Under the conditions that exist on Earth today, greenhouse gases are emitted by volcanoes, but carbon dioxide dissolves in water which trickles over and through the rocks, where chemical reactions take carbon dioxide and use it in making rocks such as limestone. This weathering helps to keep things in balance. If the planet warms a little, there is more evaporation from the oceans, so there is more rain and more weathering, which draws carbon dioxide out of the air, so the greenhouse effect is reduced, and the world cools. When the world cools a little, the opposite happens. Human activities are in the process of upsetting this balance, but without us it has kept the temperature of the Earth stable within a relatively narrow range for millions of years, not least thanks to the hydrogen bonding which gives water its unusual properties.

During a snowball era, the Earth is so cold, with the equator as cold as the heart of Antarctica today, that there is essentially no weathering, so carbon dioxide can build up over a long period of time to the point where the temperature rises and a thaw sets in. As the ice retreats, dark surface is revealed, and this absorbs solar warmth, raising temperatures further. But geologists estimate that the big thaw must take several million years to complete, after a snowball phase lasting tens of millions of years. Such thaws might be a major factor in our existence.

The snowball Earth event 2.5 billion years ago coincides, if that is the right word, with one of the most significant developments in the history of life on Earth. Just as the world was warming up again, huge amounts of oxygen were released into the air by the first organisms that evolved the ability to use carbon dioxide as food and release free oxygen through photosynthesis – single-celled creatures called cyanobacteria. This was a two-fold evolutionary advantage. To previous organisms oxygen was a poison that had to be locked away in harmless compounds, at the cost of energy. The new species could not only live with oxygen and save energy, but by releasing oxygen they poisoned all their rivals. The effect on the physical environment was equally dramatic. Free oxygen in the air and ocean reacted with iron compounds to form huge deposits of iron oxides seen in rocks around the world and known as 'banded iron formations'. As the world warmed out of the snowball state, it also rusted, thanks to the spread of photosynthesising life. Is it really a coincidence that a major evolutionary leap occurred just as life burst out of whatever niches it had survived in during the snowball Earth just as the world warmed? Probably not, although we may never know for sure.

We have a much better idea of how life exploded across the planet at the end of the most recent snowball phase, and much more compelling evidence that the thaw gave a boost to evolution.

Environmental stress can boost evolution by killing off successful species and allowing the survivors (assuming there are any) to adapt and evolve to take their place. The classic example is the death of the dinosaurs some 65 million years ago, which left empty ecological niches for the mammals to fill and adapt to, eventually producing ourselves. But the dinosaurs were only there themselves because of what happened about 600 million years ago.

This was before life had moved out of the sea and onto the land, so the species that survived the snowball must have been localised in rare warm places, perhaps associated with volcanic regions, where there was liquid water in puddles (reminiscent of Darwin's warm little pond). These survivors included bacteria, and larger single-celled organisms such as algae. Around the time that all this was happening, the first multicellular creatures, rather like sponges, evolved. This is just the sort of development that you might expect in an isolated warm little pond where new 'ideas' could get a start without much risk of being eaten by rivals. But it was just after the thaw that things got really interesting. Around 570 million years ago there was a proliferation of multicellular life so dramatic that it is used as the marker for the beginning of a new era of geological time, the Cambrian. It is often referred to as the 'Cambrian explosion'. Complex organisms of great variety evolved in the oceans at this time, as the evolutionary advantages of multicellular life allowed them to spread. Everything before the Cambrian is lumped together by geologists as the Precambrian – some 3.5 billion years of Earth history during which life was only represented by single-celled organisms. The few hundred million years since the Cambrian explosion contain almost everything that we multicelled creatures regard as important, with life moving out of the sea onto the land and producing things as diverse as dinosaurs, oak trees, orchids and us. And it all began when the world warmed out of the most recent snowball state.

There are two messages to carry away from all this. The first is that hydrogen bonding is, from a human perspective, the most important pillar of science. It is responsible for the molecules of life, and, literally, for the water of life. The second message is that life is dramatically affected by things like snowball epochs. Without the snowball event 700 million to 600 million years ago and the subsequent Cambrian explosion we would not be here. And this is not the only bottleneck in the story of how life forms like us emerged on a planet like the Earth.

EPILOGUE

Bottlenecks: Maybe We Are Alone

What can the seven pillars of science tell us about our place in the Universe? The steps which led to the emergence of life on Earth are clear, and suggest that life is common in the Universe. But the possibility of other life forms like us, intelligent creatures with a technological civilisation, is much less clear. The technological qualification is important. By many criteria whales and dolphins are as intelligent as us, but they do not build radio telescopes and spaceships; if we are to make contact with other intelligent life in the Universe, it will be with creatures that do have that kind of technology. From now on, if I refer to intelligent life without qualification, I mean that kind of life. So why are *we* here, rather than 'only' dolphins and whales, butterflies and oak trees, or dinosaurs?

With only one example of a planet with this kind of intelligent life, it is unwise to generalise. But I shall do so anyway. One striking feature of our existence is how long it has taken for us to appear, both in terms of the age of the Universe and in terms of the age of the Earth. Our Solar System formed some 4.5 billion years ago, about 9 billion years after the Universe emerged from the Big Bang. There is a reason why it took so long for the Sun and its family of stars to form. The first stars were composed only of hydrogen and helium, and there were no heavy elements associated with them from which planets could form. Generations of stars had to run through their life cycles and spread heavier elements through interstellar space before even the small portion we find in the Solar System had built up in the cloud from which the Sun and planets formed. Using their understanding of the way stars evolve, and observations of our own island in space, the Milky Way, astronomers calculate that there is a 'Galactic Habitable Zone', or GHZ.

The Sun is part of a disc-shaped collection of stars, the Milky Way galaxy, about 100,000 light years across and 1,000 light years thick. Close to the centre of the Milky Way, there are many stars relatively close together, some of which explode as supernovas or kilonovas. This produces an abundance of heavy elements, from which planets can form around later generations of stars, but the radiation from these explosions is extremely harmful for life. Further out from the centre of the galaxy, there are fewer stars and less opportunity for heavy elements to build up. But in a ring around the Milky Way roughly 26,000 light years out from the centre, by about 5 billion years ago heavy elements had built up to the concentration we see in the Solar System, and stars like the Sun could form. We are close to the centre of this GHZ.

Once the Earth formed, as we have seen, life got started with almost indecent haste. But for more than 3 billion years this consisted only of single-celled organisms living in the sea. One inference from this is that even on Earth-like planets in our neck of the cosmic woods, that is the most likely kind of life to find. Was the emergence of multicellular life and the colonisation of the land inevitable? Or did it require a special event – a snowball Earth event – to trigger these developments?

Just as there is a Galactic Habitable Zone, so there is a Stellar Habitable Zone, or SHZ, defined as the region around a star where life forms like us can exist. The simplest rule of thumb is that this is the region where the temperature at the surface of a planet is between 0°C and 100°C, the range where, thanks to hydrogen bonding, liquid water can exist. The Earth is almost in the middle of the Sun's SHZ. As I pointed out earlier, the next planet in towards the Sun, Venus, although otherwise a prime candidate for the label 'Earth-like', is too hot. The next planet out from the Sun, Mars, is too cold today, although it may once have had a thick enough atmosphere for the greenhouse effect to bring its surface temperature into the critical range. Unfortunately, partly because it is a small planet with a weak gravitational pull, it has lost most of that atmosphere. This has led to astronomers coming up with another of their beloved acronyms, CHZ, for Continuously Habitable Zone. The Earth is near the middle of the Sun's CHZ, which extends only from about 5 per cent closer to the Sun than we are to 1 per cent farther out from the Sun than we are. The important point is that judging from how long it has taken for our kind of intelligent life to emerge on Earth, a planet does indeed need to be continuously habitable, at least for billions of years, to produce technological civilisation. If there ever was life on Mars, it never had the time to evolve into creatures like us. These are sobering considerations to set against the euphoria of headline stories about new discoveries of planets orbiting other stars.

The kind of orbits those planets are in also hints that there is something unusual about our Solar System. 'Our' planets go round the Sun in roughly circular orbits, and are spaced far enough apart that they do not have a great influence on one another. In other planetary systems, the orbits tend to be more elliptical – this rule holds particularly well for giant planets similar to Jupiter, the largest planet in our Solar System, which are easier to study. It is easy to understand how planets get into such orbits; this is the natural state for them to form in. It is hard to understand how the planets of our Solar System got themselves into neat circular orbits, and astronomers still argue over this. But the fact is that they are in such tidy orbits. You can imagine the chaos it would cause if Jupiter did have a significantly elliptical orbit, maybe moving in on each circuit of the Solar System as close to the Sun as the Earth is now, before swinging back out to the distance of Saturn today. Its gravitational pull would disrupt the orbits of any inner planets, which clearly would not be continuously habitable. By contrast, in its actual orbit Jupiter seems to have been a benevolent influence, helping to stabilise the Solar System and keeping the Earth habitable.

Jupiter, which has more than 300 times the mass of the Earth, has such a strong gravitational attraction that it has played a large part in the evolution of the Solar System. Early on, it was involved in shaking up the orbits of the bits of cosmic rubble left over from the formation of the planets that resulted in the Late Heavy Bombardment mentioned in Pillar Four. Once most of the debris had been cleared during this process, the rest was tugged by Jupiter into reasonably circular orbits between Mars and Jupiter, the asteroid belt, where it mostly remained. But there was also debris, in the form of ice-covered rocky material, left over in the outer part of the Solar System, beyond the orbits of the planets. This region is the source of comets which come in past the giant planets to the inner part of the Solar System and swing past the Sun, growing glowing tails as the icy stuff is evaporated by solar heating. Jupiter also captures many of these objects that might otherwise come in past the Earth, or even collide with our planet. This was spectacularly demonstrated in July 1994, when an incoming comet known as Shoemaker-Levy 9 was ripped apart by Jupiter's gravity and the fragments collided with the giant planet.

Even with Jupiter sweeping up much of this cosmic debris, some does still get through to the inner Solar System. The geological evidence reveals that the Earth has been hit by an object at least 10 km across once every hundred million years or so. This is about the size of the impact that struck our planet some 65 million years ago and caused a massive

Impact of Shoemaker-Levy 9 with Jupiter
201010 Ltd/Science Photo Library

extinction of life on Earth, including the death of the dinosaurs. It has taken all that time for the shrew-like survivors
of that disaster to have evolved our technological civilisation.
Without Jupiter shielding us from such events, an impact like
that would occur roughly every 10,000 years. There would be
no chance to develop intelligence in such a short time, even
if any complex life survived on land at all.

There are also threats to life on Earth from within our
planet, not just from outside. About 250 million years ago,
the Earth experienced a volcanic event (the word hardly seems
strong enough!) which lasted for about a million years and
spread lava to form a thick layer of rocks known as the Siberian
Traps across what is now – you guessed – Siberia. This event
and its associated impact on the atmosphere and climate of the
entire planet caused an extinction of life which killed about
90 per cent of all species around at the time, marking the end
of the Permian era of geological time and the beginning of
the Triassic.

There is also evidence of supervolcanoes on a smaller scale
in the much more recent geological past. These include one
that produced Lake Toba, in Indonesia, about 70,000 years
ago. This was the largest known eruption of the past 25 million years. It spread a layer of ash roughly 15 cm deep over the
entire Indian subcontinent, and while all that material and
gases from the eruption were in the atmosphere it would have
had a dramatic effect on climate. The environmental changes
clearly had an impact on our ancestors. DNA evidence tells

us that at just about the time of the Indonesian eruption the entire human population of the planet fell to about a thousand people. This is worth reiterating. The entire human population of the Earth, perhaps as little as a few hundred couples, only survived the catastrophe in an isolated pocket in East Africa. These numbers are so small that any species which existed today in such a precarious isolated population would be officially classified as endangered. We scraped through that bottleneck by the skin of our teeth.

You might feel reassured by the fact that this was indeed the largest eruption of the past 25 million years, and that we did survive. Surely there won't be another one soon? Think again. The entire region underneath Yellowstone Park in the United States is now known to be a supervolcano like this waiting to blow its top. Sooner or later it will erupt; we can only hope that it will be later rather than sooner.

The overall message is clear. The Earth is subject to repeated catastrophes, some from within, some from without – and I have not even mentioned events like 'ordinary' ice ages. On our planet, there has been time in one of the gaps between catastrophes for a technological civilisation to emerge, but only just. There is also some evidence that our planet is particularly favoured in this regard. The Solar System has been in the right part of the Milky Way at the right time to form planets like the Earth, and the unusual arrangement of the planets in our Solar System, especially the beneficial influence of Jupiter, has made the intervals between catastrophes unusually long. Does all this mean that even though life must be common in the Universe, intelligent life like us is rare and Bruno was wrong after all? You will have to make up your own mind about that, but my personal conclusion is that we are probably alone.

NOTES

1. See Andrew Weiner, https://www.jstor.org/stable/437245
2. *Six Easy Pieces*, Basic Books; 4th revised edition (7 April 2011).
3. From his *Autobiographical Notes*, edited by P.A. Schilpp, Open Court, Illinois, 1979.
4. *Science*, Volume 39, p. 791.

FURTHER READING

Easy Stuff

Richard Feynman, *Six Easy Pieces*, Basic Books, New York, revised edition, 2011

Steven Weinberg, *The First Three Minutes*, Basic Books, New York, revised edition, 1993

John Gribbin, *Stardust*, Penguin, London, 2009

Horace Freeland Judson, *The Eighth Day of Creation*, Cape, London, 1979

James Lovelock, *Gaia*, Oxford University Press, new edition, 2016

Not so easy stuff

Alexander Oparin, *The Origin of Life*, Dover, New York, revised edition, 1953

Linus Pauling, *The Nature of the Chemical Bond*, Oxford University Press, revised edition, 1960

Erwin Schrödinger, *What is Life?*, Cambridge University Press, 1944 (reprinted in 1967)

Hard stuff

Selected Genetic Papers of J.B.S. Haldane, Routledge, London, reprint of 1990 edition, 2015; also available on Kindle

Entertaining stuff

Fred Hoyle, *The Black Cloud*, Penguin Classics edition, 2010

SIX IMPOSSIBLE THINGS

*The 'Quanta of Solace' and
the Mysteries of the Subatomic World*

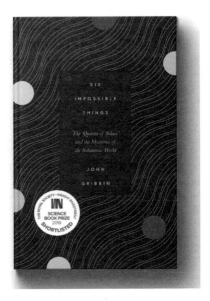

**SHORTLISTED FOR THE ROYAL SOCIETY
INSIGHT INVESTMENT SCIENCE BOOK PRIZE 2019**

Quantum physics is very strange. For the past hundred years, no one has managed to explain what is really going on in the subatomic world. So physicists have sought 'quanta of solace' in a startling array of interpretations.

Six Impossible Things takes us on a mindbending tour through the 'big six', including the Copenhagen interpretation and the pilot wave and 'many worlds' approaches.

All are crazy, some more crazy than others. But in quantum physics crazy does not necessarily mean wrong. John Gribbin – who has spent a lifetime unravelling complex science – presents a dazzlingly succinct guide to a truly bizarre world.

ISBN 978-178578-499-6

£9.99